KUNSTHISTORISCHES MUSEUM

SCHATZKAM.

(The Crown Jewels and the Ecclesiastical Treasure Chamber)

BY
HERMANN FILLITZ

TRANSLATED BY
GEOFFREY HOLMES

3rd edition

VIENNA 1963

Kunsthistorisches Museum
Guide No. 5

© Copyright 1963 and 1974 (reprint)
by Kunsthistorisches Museum, Vienna
Photographs: Kunsthistorisches Museum, Vienna
Photo Meyer KG, Vienna
Printed by Friedrich Jasper, Vienna
Printed in Austria

This guide is a shortened and revised edition of the German-language "Katalog der Weltlichen und der Geistlichen Schatzkammer", guide No. 2 to the Kunsthistorisches Museum, Vienna 1954, by the same author. The text of this guide has been adjusted to the non-German speaking public, less important objects have been dealt with collectively, and the apparatus of scholarship has been curtailed. Bibliographical references have been entirely omitted. The reader who is interested in a more profound study is referred to the larger Guide to the Treasure Chamber in German.

Conversely, however, a list of the emperors and kings of the Holy Roman Empire and a genealogical table of the most important Habsburgs from Leopold I onwards have been added to facilitate an understanding of this catalogue.

*

Originally, a treasure chamber included everything of such value to the possessor that he kept it safe in a strong vault against the attacks of intruders, fire or other dangers. A variety of things came into this category: precious metal, in coins or in bars, costly tableware, jewels, ornament, works of art, but also deeds and finally the insignia, which were the symbol and proof of the position and power of their owner. Here were stored mementoes and heirlooms of special significance. Lastly, relics and reliquaries were kept here, which were valued not only as a security for the life beyond, but also partly as a guarantee and visible proof of the spiritual position of the ruler. According to mediaeval belief, they were of active assistance in the achievement of worldly aims; already in the 14th century this section was designated as "ecclesiastical" as distinct from the secular treasure house.

The new thought of the Renaissance transformed the character of the treasure chamber. Aesthetic and intellectual elements and curious now outweigh the purely valuable; articles of worldly fortune — precious metals, precious stones, currency and deeds — were removed from the treasure chamber, which could now be more accurately described as a "Chamber of Art and Wonders". Indeed the foundations were laid here for later collections and museums arranged on the basis of sound scholarship; this step, however, remained to be taken by the Baroque age.

The treasuries of the Renaissance are still formed completely by the taste and interests of their owners. The first collections of this kind are to be found in the 15th century in France, at the courts of the royal family of Valois, of the Dukes of Berry and above all the court of the Burgundian Dukes. When the male branch of the Burgundian Valois died out with Charles the Bold, who fell in the Battle of Nancy (1477), his daughter and heiress Maria married the Archduke Maximilian, and in this way the most important late mediaeval treasure passed into the hands of the Habsburgs. The great rise of this family in the course of the 16th century was quite naturally reflected in the art collections which were now, starting with Emperor Ferdinand I, continuously expanded: in the process, the special orientation of the collections was dictated by individual personalities. Among these, Ferdinand's son, the Archduke Ferdinand of Tirol, and his grandson Emperor Rudolph II, are the most striking figures. While the former built up his collections at Castle Ambras in Tirol, the most important part of which comprised weapons and armour, the latter brought together an almost unbelievable treasure of valuables and all kinds of works of art in the Hradschin in Prague. There too, he established, with leading goldsmiths, engravers, enamelists, etc. from many different countries, a unified workshop, the "Imperial Court Workshop". Their most important work consists of the Crown, the Sceptre and the Imperial Orb, ordered by Emperor Rudolph II and his brother and successor Matthias. On account of their costliness, and their superlative artistic quality, they subsequently always stood at the forefront of the goldsmith's works of the treasure chamber, were designated as family insignia and from time to time used as such.

It was also Emperor Matthias who ordered the Prague art collection to be brought to Vienna and combined with the collection that had been created here by Emperor Ferdinand I and Maximilian II. In the third decade of the 18th century the treasure chamber was brought into the rooms of the "Alte Burg" (Old Castle) where is still is today. The iron entry door with the monogram of Emperor Charles VI dates from this time (1712). His daughter Maria Theresia then ordered a completely new arrangement of the treasure chamber, whose principal task it was to place on view the treasure of the House of Habsburg as attractively as possible. Some of the magnificent display cases, which were made for the purpose in 1747, are still preserved in the rooms of the ecclesiastical treasure chamber. The treasure was enriched at this time by the precious objects which Franz Stephan of Lorraine brought into his marriage with Maria Theresia. They consisted principally of ornaments richly studded with diamonds and precious stones. The most famous of them was the "Florentine", one of the largest diamonds in existence.

After the death of Empress Maria Theresia, when her son Joseph II assumed the throne alone, he placed the ecclesiastical treasure chamber under the care of the Castle chaplain. In this way it was joined with the treasure in use in the Castle Chapel. In particular, the unique set of baroque paraments in the ecclesiastical treasure chamber derives its origin from this time.

The troubled period of the Napoleonic wars and the revolutions of the 19th century brought the treasure chamber considerable accretions. The most important of them are the Insignia and Regalia of the Holy Roman Empire, which were transferred to the Imperial treasure house at the command of Emperor Franz I from Nürnberg and Aachen, in 1800 and 1801 respectively, during the retreat from Napoleon. After the first World War, which ended in tragedy for Austria, it suffered again some considerable losses: in 1918 the Imperial family took with them into exile their private jewelry which had been kept in the Treasure chamber; two years later the insignia and vestment of Napoleon as king of Italy had to be delivered to the Italian State. Finally, in 1932 a request of Hungary had to be met for the vestment of the Order of St. Stephen, the Order's Cross, studded with diamonds, both once belonging to Empress Maria Theresia, and the two caskets in which the Hungarian coronation gift was handed over in 1867.

Following the end of the Monarchy, the administration of the Crown jewels and the Ecclesiastical treasure chamber was taken over by the Kunsthistorisches Museum. In 1938, when the Insignia and Regalia of the Holy Roman Empire were taken to Nürnberg at the order of Hitler, the treasure chamber had to be shut. It was then no longer possible to arrange a new exhibition of the reduced treasure. In the year 1946, the Insignia of the Holy Roman Empire were brought back to Vienna. Like the other articles belonging to the Crown Jewels, they fortunately survived the war undamaged, so far as could be judged up to the present.

The Treasure chamber has been opened to the public again since 1st July 1954, in its old rooms, but with a new arrangement.

The order of the catalogue follows that of the rooms. The Secular Treasury is arranged according to certain main themes, while the Ecclesiastical section is arranged chronologically. Within the individual rooms of the Secular section, priority has generally been given to the order of precedence of exhibits rather than to considerations of visual balance. The material designation of individual objects is normally limited to their visible parts. The designation following in parenthesis is the inventory number. In hallmark references, the abbreviation R3 refers to Marc Rosenberg: "Der Goldschmiede Merkzeichen", third edition (new impression 1955).

It should be noted that in this new edition of the catalogue the basic arrangement and numbering of exhibits have been preserved, even where individual items were excluded (Nos. 129 and 132 of the Secular section, No. 23 of the Ecclesiastical Treasure Chamber), or where new items were added (40 a, 85 a, 96 a, 96 b, 96 c, 113 a, 122, 144 a in the former section, 6 a, 13 a and 121 in the latter). Some items have been newly acquired. In the Ecclesiastical Treasure Chamber, the items Nos. 21 and 26 are newly exhibited vestments, the former being exhibited for the first time after careful restoration.

HISTORICAL EXPLANATIONS

In the course of history the Habsburgs assumed various dignities, a short explanation of which is necessary to understand the insignia and vestments displayed in the Treasure chamber. These dignities are entirely independent of each other.

1. EMPEROR OR KING OF THE HOLY ROMAN EMPIRE

The Holy Roman Empire was established with the coronation of Emperor Charlemagne on Christmas Day in the year 800. This event assured the continuation of the Roman Empire (imperium romanum) in the Christian Occident. Its ideal king was Christ, Lord of all the world. His deputy on earth was the Emperor. In practise, the Holy Roman Empire coincided with the area ruled by the king of Germany. For this reason it has, since the 15th century, been unofficially called the "Holy Roman Empire of the German nation". The king of the Empire was usually crowned at Aachen by the Archbishops of Cologne, Mainz and Trier; since the 16th century at Frankfurt-on-the-Main. He could then receive the Imperial crown from the Pope, usually at St. Peter's in Rome. When the Republic of Venice refused Maximilian I passage through its territory, he received permission from the Pope to assume the title *"Elected Roman Emperor"*. This title was then born by all his successors on the throne of the Holy Roman Empire. Only Emperor Charles V was afterwards crowned by the Pope, this time in the cathedral of Bologna. In 1806 Emperor Franz II declared the Holy Roman Empire dissolved.

2. EMPEROR OF AUSTRIA

In 1804, Emperor Franz II (as such, Emperor of the Holy Roman Empire) assumed the title of Emperor of Austria (as such, Emperor Franz I) at the same time as Napoleon had himself crowned as Emperor of the French. Through this he gathered the whole of his crown lands to the Empire without thereby changing in any way the character of the different lands. The Kingdom of Hungary, the Kingdom of Bohemia and the Austrian patrimonial dominions thus remained unaffected by this measure.

3. KING OF HUNGARY AND KING OF BOHEMIA

On the occasion of the double marriage in the year 1515, when Ferdinand and Maria, grandchildren of Emperor Maximilian I, were married to Louis of the Jagellon dynasty, heir to the throne of Hungary and Bohemia, and his sister Anna, the two reigning houses came to the following agreement: if one of the two lines should die out, then the other would have the right of succession to the throne. A mere eleven years later this agreement became applicable, when Louis fell in the battle of Mohacs (1526) leaving no children. From then onwards the Habsburgs were also King of Hungary and King of Bohemia. The insignia of these kingdoms (crown of St. Stephen's and crown of Wenzel) never belonged to the Treasury in Vienna, except for a short while during the reign of Joseph II.

4. ARCHDUKE OF AUSTRIA

Through the forgery of the "privilegium maius" Duke Rudolph IV (1339 to 1365) claimed the title of Archduke for himself and his heirs. This deed assumed legal validity through its ratification by Emperor Frederick II, so that the Habsburgs have since then born this title, which gave every one of them precedence over the dukes. Geographically speaking, the title "Archduchy" referred to Austria above the river Enns, and Austria below that river (the Upper and Lower Austria of today). On the other hand the *Austrian patrimonial dominions* included the counties of Styria, Carinthia, Görz, Krain, Tyrol, the possessions in south-western Germany (the remainder of which is now the province of Vorarlberg) and since 1805 the old Prince-Archbishopric of Salzburg.

THE EMPERORS AND KINGS OF THE HOLY ROMAN EMPIRE FROM HENRY I TO THE DISSOLUTION OF THE EMPIRE

Henry I	919— 936	
Otto I the Great	936— 973	
Otto II	973— 983	Saxon Emperors and Kings
Otto III	983—1002	
Henry II the Saint	1002—1024	
Konrad II	1024—1039	
Henry III	1039—1056	Frankish (or Salian) Emperors
Henry IV	1056—1105	and Kings
Henry V	1105—1125	
Lothar of Saxony	1125—1137	
Konrad III	1138—1152	
Frederick I Barbarossa	1152—1190	
Henry VI	1190—1197	
Philip of Brunswick	1198—1208	
Otto IV	1198—1218	Swabian Emperors and Kings and their rivals
Frederick II	1212—1250	
Heinrich Raspe	1246—1247	
William of Holland	1247—1256	
Konrad IV	1250—1254	
Richard, earl of Cornwall	1257—1272	
Alfons X of Castille	1257, †1284	
Rudolf I of Habsburg	1273—1291	
Adolf of Nassau	1292—1298	
Albrecht I of Habsburg	1298—1308	
Henry IV of Luxembourg	1308—1313	
Frederick the Fair (Habsburg)	1314, captured by Ludwig of Bavaria 1322, †1330	

Ludwig of Bavaria	1314—1347
Charles IV of Luxembourg	1346—1378
Wenzel of Luxembourg	1378—1400
Rupprecht of the Palatinate	1400—1410
Sigismund of Luxembourg	1410—1437

Albrecht II	1438—1439	
Frederick III	1440—1493	
Maximilian I	1493—1519	
Charles V	1519—1556	
Ferdinand I	1556—1564	
Maximilian II	1564—1576	
Rudolph II	1576—1612	} Habsburg Emperors and Kings
Matthias	1612—1619	
Ferdinand II	1619—1637	
Ferdinand III	1637—1657	
Leopold I	1658—1705	
Joseph I	1705—1711	
Charles VI (Charles III of Spain)	1711—1740	

Charles VII of Bavaria	1742—1745
Franz I (Stephan of Lorraine)	1745—1765

Joseph II	1765—1790	
Leopold II	1790—1792	} The House of Habsburg-Lorraine
Franz II	1792—1806	

GENEALOGICAL TABLE OF THE EMPERORS OF THE HOUSES OF HABSBURG AND HABSBURG-LORRAINE FROM LEOPOLD I.

Leopold I.
1640—1705

Joseph I.
1678—1711

Charles VI.
1685—1740

Maria Theresia
1717—1780

∞ 1736

Franz Stephan, Duke of Lorraine, as Emperor Franz I.
1708—1765

Joseph II.
1741—1790

Leopold II.
1747—1792

Franz II. (as Emperor of Austria Franz I)
1768—1835

Ferdinand I., the Kind
1795—1875
(abdicated as Emperor 1848)

Franz
1802—1878

Franz Joseph I.
1830—1916

Rudolph
1858—1889

Maximilian
Emperor of Mexico
1832—1867

Karl Ludwig
1833—1896

Franz Ferdinand
1863—1914

Otto
1865—1906

Charles I.
1887—1918, † 1922

THE CROWN JEWELS

I. THE INSIGNIA OF HEREDITARY HOMAGE

The so-called "hereditary homage" is a ceremonial act only to be found in this form in the Austrian lands. There was no coronation for the ruler of Austria: until 1804 he was an archduke; and thereafter no coronation was provided for in the ceremonial of the hereditary Empire of Austria (that he was crowned as Emperor of the Holy Roman Empire, as King of Hungary and King of Bohemia did not affect his relationship to the patrimonial dominions of Austria!).

Homage of representatives of the land ("hereditary officers") is thus connected with the ascension to the throne of an archduke, and is preceded by ratification of the old privileges and freedoms by the new prince of the land.

When Emperor Ferdinand I ascended the throne, the last hereditary homage for the archduchy of Austria above and below the Enns took place in Vienna in 1835; and for the county of Tyrol, in Innsbruck in 1838.

In this ceremonial act, the representatives of the land wore the insignia displayed in this room and carried out the old services of the court which court servants had otherwise performed for a long time, and some of which even had no longer any practical significance, but were only the ceremonial relics of an old custom (e. g. the insignia and offices of hawking).

1 THE BAROQUE COPY OF THE AUSTRIAN ARCHDUKE'S CORONET
   (Painting)
   Austrian, 1765.
   78·5 × 65 cm; 30 × 25⁵/₈ in. Canvas. (XIV 144)

The archduke's coronet was claimed for the Austrian rulers 'in place of the older duke's coronet by Duke Rudolph IV, the founder. The preserved official archduke's coronet was introduced in 1616, and since then has been kept with the skull relic of St. Leopold, the patron saint of Lower Austria, in the monastery at Klosterneuburg. As it was only allowed to be taken away for the official act of hereditary homage, Joseph II had a copy of it made for himself in 1764 which is kept, in a seriously damaged condition, in the vault of the Treasury. This painting represents the copy.

2 THE ORB
   Bohemian (?); second half of the 15th century.
   16 cm; 6¹/₈in. hight. Gilded silver. (XIV 43)

The Orb and the Sceptre (No. 3) originally belonged to the Bohemian coronation insignia (cf. the portrait — in the room where the tickets are issued — of Emperor Matthias as King of Bohemia). Matthias had the Sceptre and Imperial Orb specially made to go with the crown of Rudolph (cf. Nos. 56/57); he transferred to the Bohemian regalia both the insignia previously worn with the crown of Rudolph II; and transferred the gothic Orb and Sceptre from those regalia to the Austrian hereditary insignia.

3 THE SCEPTRE
   Bohemian (?); second half of the 15th century.
   80 cm; 31¹/₂ in. long. Gilded silver. (XIV 44)
   Cf. the preceding note on the Orb (No 2).

4 THE SWORD OF INVESTITURE

Hans Sumersberger (1492—1498 working in Hall, Tyrol).

139 cm; 55 in. long. Signed: MAISTER (HAN)NS VON H(ALL). Dated 1496. Steel,
azured with gold inlay; brass; silver and mother-of-pearl. (XIV 4)

The blade shows the arms of the possessions of Maximilian I. On the brass
hilt the king's crown and the archduke's hat. They are repeated at the ends
of the cross-bar. The arms on the blade also appear on the cross-bar and
pommel. The decoration is designed for the sword to be carried upright. This
is a ceremonial sword from the reign of Maximilian I, perhaps the only insignia that has been preserved from his private coronation vestments.

It is not known how long the sword has been used at hereditary homages.
Information on this point dates only from the late 19th century. It
was carried at the hereditary homage by the Grand Marshall of the patrimonial dominions. The sword was restored in 1871, at which time the false
mother-of-pearl pieces were no doubt added, and certain places ground off
such as the two edges of the blade and the upper part of the handle.

5 THE INSIGNIA OF THE GRAND FALCONER OF THE PATRIMONIAL
DOMINIONS

Vienna (?), 1835.

Consisting of:
Hawking-Pouch. Green velvet, embroidered with gold; the fastening of gilded
silver; gold cord interwoven with green silk. (XIV 36)

Two falcon's hoods. Green velvet, red and green leather with gold impres-
sions; feathers. (XIV 37, 38)

Falcon's lure: Red leather, gilded silver; gold cord interwoven with green silk
(XIV 39)

On the hawking pouch and the two falcon's hoods the monogram of Emperor
Ferdinand I of Austria.

6 THE COLLAR FOR THE HOUND, THE EMBLEM OF THE GRAND
MASTER OF THE HUNT OF THE PATRIMONIAL DOMINIONS

Vienna (?), 1835.

Green velvet, embroidered with gold; mountings of gilded silver; on a gold
cord interwoven with green silk. (XIV 40)

On the mountings the monogram of Emperor Ferdinand I of Austria.

7 THE AUSTRIAN HEREDITARY STANDARD

Austrian, 1705.

Red silk-damask, embroidered with gold, silver and silk; on a flag staff chased
with red, silver and gold; the point in gilded silver. The shoulder belt of red
velvet, embroidered with gold and silver. (XIV 34)

Next to the arms of Austria above and below the Enns, and on the tip of the
staff, are worked the arms of the Imperial Counts of Abensperg-Traun, who
were standard bearers from the time the office was created up to the end of
the Monarchy.

8 THE SHIELD OF LOWER AUSTRIA

Vienna (?), 1835.

Silver, gilded and enamelled; red velvet. (XIV 35)

9   TABARD AND STAFF OF THE HERALD OF THE LAND OF AUSTRIA
    BELOW THE ENNS
    Austrian, 18th century.
    Gold and silver lamé with gold, silver and silk embroidery. (XIV 67, 68)

10—21   VARIOUS CEREMONIAL STAFFS
    Dating from around 1600 (No. 10), from the 17th century (No. 11), 18th cen-
    tury (No. 12) and 19th century. They were used for different offices and cere-
    monies. Staff No. 20 was made for the coronation of Emperor Franz Joseph I
    as King of Hungary in the year 1867, after the design of No. 10.

22—38   CHAMBERLAIN'S KEYS
    From Emperor Charles VI to Emperor Franz Joseph I.
    These keys, originally intended for the doorkeepers of the sovereign, became
    in the 17th century merely symbols of a court honour. They are accordingly
    no longer effective for locking purposes. In the key-ring, the monogram or
    arms of the bestower. These keys, together with the tassel displayed as No. 38,
    were carried at hip level on the right of the uniform.

39, 40   BADGE OF THE DEPUTY COMMANDER OF TOURNAMENTS OF
    EMPEROR FRANZ JOSEPH I
    The deputy commander of tournaments is the dignitary subordinate to the
    Lord High Steward. His badge was carried with a tassel, in the same way as
    the Chamberlain's keys.

40 a   BADGE OF THE DEPUTY COMMANDER OF TOURNAMENTS OF
    EMPEROR FRANZ JOSEPH I., WITH A TASSEL OF EMPEROR
    CHARLES I.

41   TABARD AND STAFF OF THE HERALD OF THE PROVINCE OF TYROL
    Made in 1838 by Johann Fritz in Vienna.
    Silver lamé, silk embroidery. (XIV 71)
    The herald's staff is of wood, chased with colours. (XIV 72)

42   RIDING WHIP OF THE GRAND EQUERRY OF THE COUNTY OF TYROL
    Vienna (?), 1838.
    102 cm; 40 in. long. Plaited cane, the gilded silver fastenings partly with
    cold enamel. On the pommel the arms of Tyrol and the inscription 1838.
    (XIV 42)

43   STAFF OF THE IMPERIAL CHAMBERLAIN
    German, end of the 15th century (?).
    91 cm; 36 in. long. Rosewood, bone. (XIV 17)
    According to an unverifiable tradition, the staff which Emperor Maximilian I
    bestowed on the first Imperial Chamberlain (Eitel Friedrich, Count of Hohen-
    zollern) as the badge of his rank.

44   MAIN DE JUSTICE
    French (or west German under strong French influence), 17th century.
    64·5 cm; 25½ in. long. Silver, partly gilded. (XIV 18)
    According to tradition, used at the enfeoffment in the former possessions in
    south-western Germany.

II. ARTICLES AND ROBES FOR HOLY BAPTISM

While most of the insignia and robes belonging to the Secular Treasure chamber
are connected with the rank and office of the ruler, the articles and robes used in
baptism are distinguished from those in general use for the administration of this
sacrament only by their exquisite execution and superlative material. This was
however not merely in order to put on show the riches and power of the House
at this representative family celebration, but also to mark the special position of
the child already at his first "public appearance"; for the same reason a small
neck-chain of the Order of the Golden Fleece was laid in the cradle of the Crown
Prince, so as to indicate his future sovereignty over the Order.

Since the Treasure chamber was depleted in the late 19th century the baptismal
articles and robes are the only examples of how a substantial part of the content
of the Treasure chamber consisted formerly of the most richly executed articles
used for all kinds of representative ceremonies. The majority of these magnificent
objects are now to be found in the collections of sculpture and handicrafts of the
Kunsthistorisches Museum.

45 THE BAPTISMAL CAN AND THE BAPTISMAL BOWL
Upper Italy, 1571.
Height of the can 34·5 cm; 13⅝ in. Diameter of the bowl 61·5 cm; 24³/₈ in. The
can is dated on the handle. Gold, partly decorated with enamel. (XIV 5, 6)

This set, one of the finest of the 16th century, is the wedding present of Carinthia to Archduke Charles of Inner Austria and his bride Maria, daughter
of Duke Albrecht V of Bavaria (married on 26th August 1571). Sets of this
kind, but not so richly decorated, were used at festive banquets for washing
hands and from the late 16th century onwards were never missing from the
sideboards. Already in the 17th century the present set is known to have been
used for baptism. Instead of the heavy can, a small golden one was used in
preference (No. 46).

46 SMALL POURING CAN
Prague, Imperial Court workshop, beginning of the 17th century.
Height 15·5 cm; 6⅛ in. Gold, partly enamelled: Rubies. (XIV 7)

On the handle a split coat of arms with the escutcheon and arms of Burgundy.
This can was used for baptism in place of the heavier can belonging to the
baptismal set.

47 THE BAPTISMAL ROBES ORDERED BY EMPRESS MARIA THERESIA
Vienna (?), 1757.
White silver moiré, with rich gold embroidery and pearl trimmings. Gold lace
on the covers.
a) Coverlet (158 × 129 cm; 62 × 51 in.). Marked: MT — 1757. (XIV 8)
b) Baptismal robe. (XIV 12)
c) Pillow (70 × 41 cm; 27⁵/₈ × 16¼ in.). (XIV 13)

48 THE BAPTISMAL ROBES ORDERED BY EMPRESS MARIA LUDOVICA
WIFE OF EMPEROR LEOPOLD II.
Vienna (?), 1790.
White silver moiré with gold embroidery.
a) Coverlet (150 × 132 cm; 59¼ × 52 in.). Marked: ML — 1790. (A 171)
b) Baptismal robe. (A 173)
c) Pillow (67 × 52 cm; 26¼ × 20½ in.). (A 174)

49 CANDLE
    1868.
    Wax candle, painted with oil colours. (D 109)
    One of the candles that were used at the baptism of Archduchess Marie Valerie
    (born 22 April 1868), the youngest daughter of Emperor Franz Joseph and
    Empress Elizabeth.

50 BAPTISMAL ROBE FOR EMPEROR FRANZ JOSEPH AND HIS BROTHERS
    AND SISTERS
    Vienna (?), around 1830.
    Tulle, with bobbinwork, and sewn appliqué; pink silk. (A 208)

51 COVERLET
    Vienna (?), 1762.
    146 × 86 cm; $57^1/_2$ × $37^3/_4$ in. Silver moiré with gold lace. (XIV 10)
    According to Catholic custom, after recovering from the birth, the young
    mother, carrying her baby, receives a special blessing in the church. On this
    occasion, this coverlet was used in court circles for carrying the child.

52 BAPTISMAL ROBE
    18th century (?).
    Batiste with gold embroidery. (XIV 11)

53 BAPTISMAL CANDLE OF THE ARCHDUCHESS ELISABETH MARIE
    1883.
    Wax candle; white velvet; studs of gilded silver plate. (D 75)
    The Archduchess is the daughter of Crown Prince Rudolf and his wife
    Stephanie.

54 FIVE TAPESTRIES WITH SCENES FROM THE PASSION AND THE
    RESURRECTION OF CHRIST
    Brussels, second half of 16th century (town's mark).
    Tapestry maker Willem Segers (?, maker's mark WS).
    Gobelins Collection. (XXXII, XXXII*)

III. THE HABSBURGS AS EMPERORS AND KINGS OF THE HOLY ROMAN EMPIRE

Besides their official insignia, almost all emperors and kings possessed private ones,
which often outshone the former in richness of material and artistic design. They
served the ruler on a variety of occasions to represent his rank, while the use of
official insignia remained reserved for very special ceremonies. Since Emperor
Sigismund, in the year 1423, gave the insignia and regalia of the Holy Roman Empire, which had previously been kept by the ruler personally, into the keeping of
Nürnberg, the emperors and kings of the Holy Roman Empire could use the official insignia of the Empire only at the coronation itself.
They were thus obliged to have private insignia and vestments made for the numerous occasions on which they had to appear in full state.
Most of these private regalia of the late Middle Ages and Renaissance were subsequently melted down again. The objects displayed here have alone been preserved.

55 THE CROWN OF EMPEROR RUDOLPH II — AFTER 1804 THE AUSTRIAN
IMPERIAL CROWN

Prague, Imperial Court workshop, 1602.

28·6 cm; 11¼ in. high. Gold; enamel; diamonds, rubies, one sapphire; pearls.
(XI a 1)

The crown was intended as a symbol of the highest dignities of Rudolph,
who was Emperor of the Holy Roman Empire, King of Hungary and King of
Bohemia. The reliefs show characteristic scenes of the three coronations:
Rudolf receives the crown of the Holy Roman Empire in Frankfurt cathedral; he is seen riding on the coronation hill at Pressburg (Hungarian coronation); and goes in solemn procession to the Hradschin at Prague (Bohemian
coronation); the fourth relief shows an allegory of his defeat of the Turks.

In its form the crown has affinities with earlier models of the late Middle
Ages which are only known to us from paintings. The mitre and the single
arch are prerogatives of the Emperor. The exact meaning of the choice of
precious stones is still unknown. It is above all characteristic that with all
the richness of detail, one large sapphire surmounts the whole. The same is
true of the imperial orb and sceptre.

The crown is the principal achievement of the workshop that Rudolph II
established at the Hradschin, in which he employed leading craftsmen among
the goldsmiths and cutters of precious stones of many countries. Unfortunately
sible for it. Rudolph's successors kept the crown with their other treasures and
none of the craftsmen who worked on the crown is known by name; it is
nevertheless assumed that Rudolph's Court goldsmith Jan Vermeyen is respon-
wore it as Emperor of the Holy Roman Empire. (Nobody was crowned with
it however. For coronations the official Imperial Crown [cf. No. 152] was
used.) When, in the year 1804, Austria was then elevated to the dignity of
an Empire, Emperor Franz I of Austria chose it as the official Austrian
Imperial Crown. It was, however, never worn in this capacity.

Through the repeated removal of precious stones and pearls, which were replaced only later, parts of the circlet were probably also lost, so that today
various holes are visible.

56 THE IMPERIAL ORB — AFTER 1804 THE AUSTRIAN IMPERIAL ORB

*Prague, Imperial Court workshop, beginning of 17th century (certainly
after 1612).*

27·4 cm; 10¾ in. high. Gold; enamel; diamonds, rubies, one sapphire; pearls.
(XI a 3)

The Imperial Orb and Sceptre (No. 57) were made under Emperor Matthias,
the brother and successor of Rudolph II, to complement the crown (No. 55).
Rudolph probably used with his crown those articles which were then transferred after the death of Emperor Matthias to the Bohemian regalia; they are
still preserved with them today in Prague.

The Imperial Orb is probably the work of the same craftsman who made the
Sceptre, i. e. Andreas Osenbruck, a Court goldsmith of Emperor Matthias. In
accordance with his commission, its construction follows the ornamentation
of the crown.

57 THE SCEPTRE — AFTER 1804 THE AUSTRIAN IMPERIAL SCEPTRE

*Andreas Osenbruck (1612—1617 Court goldsmith of Emperor Matthias), Prague
1612—1615.*

75·5 cm; 29¾ in. long. "Ainkhürn" (narwhal horn); gold; enamel; diamonds,
rubies, one sapphire; pearls. (XI a 2)

The choice of material on symbolic grounds is here especially clear in the Unicorn as the handle.

For the characteristics and significance of the Unicorn cf. the notes on No. 81.

58 EMPEROR RUDOLPH II

Adriaen de Vries (born at The Hague 1546, died at Prague 1627), 1607.

Height 54·5 cm; 21¹/₂ in. Bronze; marble. Collections of Sculpture and Handicrafts. (5491)

Signed: ADRIANVS · FRIES · HAGIENSIS · FECIT · 1607.

59 THE CROWN OF STEPHAN BOCSKAY

Turkish, beginning of 17th century.

Height 23·5 cm; 9¹/₄ in. Gold with niello; rubies; emeralds; turquoises; pearls; pink and light green (very faded) silk. (XIV 25)

Sent to Prince Stephan Bocskay of Transylvania by Sultan Achmed I through Grand Vizier Mohammed Pascha in the year 1605 as token of the acknowledgement of his rule, which he had enforced in the rising against Emperor Rudolph II; the sending of a crown by the Sublime Porte continues a Byzantine tradition. Such gifts were also intended to express the sender's superiority; this was also the case here, for mountainous Transylvania was the only part of Hungary which could successfully defend its independence of the Turks. Stephan Bocskay had the small cross added at the front of the crown. When Archduke Matthias — subsequently Emperor — tried to restore the old order in Hungary, this crown fell into his hands. It was brought to Vienna in 1610.

60 CASE FOR THE CROWN OF STEPHAN BOCSKAY

Turkish, beginning of the 17th century.

Height 26·3 cm; 18³/₈ in. Wood, covered with Persian silk brocade from the workshop of the Court of Shah Abbâs the Great (1587—1628); brass mountings. (XIV 184)

61 THE VESTMENTS OF EMPEROR FRANZ I (STEPHAN OF LORRAINE)

(The so-called Baroque copies of vestments of the Insignia of the Empire.)

Vienna, before 1764.

The vestments consist of: a) Mantle, b) Alb, c) Dalmatic, d) Stole, e) Girdle, f) Sword-belt, g) Gloves, h) Hose, i) Shoes, j) Sabre.

These were copied from the corresponding articles of the Insignia of the Empire (cf. the originals Nos. 163—173). Paper copies were prepared of the originals in Nürnberg, and sent to Vienna where the vestments were made according to these replica. Emperor Franz I ordered them to be made for himself at the coronation of his son Joseph (II) as Roman-German King on 27th March 1764 at Frankfurt-on-the-Main. He wore them there together with the "House Regalia" — i. e. the Crown of Emperor Rudolph II and the Sceptre and Imperial Orb, which Emperor Matthias had ordered to go with them. As the son was crowned with the genuine insignia, the father on this occasion had to use private vestments. These were not prepared according to new designs, but represent copies of the venerable vestments of the Crown Treasure of the Holy Roman Empire. There thus occurred the unique and instructive event of both princes emerging from the cathedral in identical vestments. Goethe, who was present at this coronation, describes the scene in detail in the 5th book of "Dichtung und Wahrheit".

Of the numerous private vestments of the Holy Roman Emperors, this is the only set has been preserved.

62 TABARD OF THE HERALD OF THE ROMAN EMPEROR
German, 1613.
Gold brocade, black silk, embroidered in colours. (XIV 100)
The breast-plate with the arms was substituted for the old arms of Emperor
Matthias at the coronation of Emperor Leopold II (1790).

63 TABARD OF THE HERALD OF THE ROMAN-GERMAN KING
German, 1st half of the 17th century.
Gold brocade, black silk, embroidered. (XIV 102)

64 TABARD AND STAFFS OF THE HERALD OF THE KING OF HUNGARY
Vienna (?), 18th century.
Red gold lamé with rich embroidery in silver. (XIV 59)
The two herald's staffs:
a) Iron, partly gilded; velvet. (XIV 61)
   German, 17th century.
b) Wood, chased in colours. (XIV 62)
   Vienna, end of 18th century.

65 TABARD AND STAFF OF THE HERALD OF THE KING OF BOHEMIA
German, 17th century.
Velvet with silver embroidery. (XIV 63)
The *herald's staff:* wood, chased in colours. (XIV 64)

65 a TABARD AND STAFF OF THE HERALD OF THE ARCHDUCHY OF
AUSTRIA
17th century.
Velvet, silver rep. (XIV 69)
Belonged to one set with the Burgundian tabards (Nos. 123 et seq.)
The herald's staff covered with velvet and silver rep; the mountings are of
brass. (XIV 70)

65 b TABARD OF A HERALD OF EMPRESS MARIA THERESIA
After 1754.
Velvet, silver lamé, gold lamé. (XIV 99)

66 FOUR RELIEFS REPRESENTING THE EVANGELISTS
German, about 1636.
Heights: 8·1 cm; 3$^1/_4$ in. 8·2 cm; 3$^1/_2$ in. 8·1 cm; 3$^1/_4$ in. 8·3 cm; 3$^3/_4$ in. Gilded
silver. Collections of Sculpture and Handicrafts (1006, 1007, 1008, 1009).
Remains of a private crown, which Emperor Ferdinand II had made and
which he is supposed to have worn for the first time at the coronation of
Ferdinand III (1636). It was a copy of the crown of the Holy Roman Empire
(No. 152).

67 EMPEROR FRANZ I
*Martin von Meytens (born 24th June 1695 in Stockholm, died 23rd March 1770
in Vienna).*
150 × 117 cm; 59$^1/_4$ × 46$^1/_4$ in. Oil on canvas. Picture-gallery. (3440)

IV. THE EMPIRE OF AUSTRIA

On 11th August 1804, Emperor Franz II proclaimed the patrimonial Empire of Austria, at a time when the imminent dissolution of the Holy Roman Empire loomed ever nearer in the light of the victories of Napoleon. As the State symbol of the new empire he chose the crown of Emperor Rudolph II, with which the Sceptre and Imperial Orb of Emperor Matthias were raised to the dignity of official insignia. As patrimonial Emperor of Austria, he is Emperor Franz I.

The new empire comprised the whole lands of the House of Habsburg, i. e. first of all the Austrian patrimonial dominions and the Kingdoms of Hungary and Bohemia. When, after the fall of Napoleon, the map of Europe was redrawn at the Congress of Vienna, the Italian provinces that Austria won back were combined into the Kingdom of Lombardy and Venetia.

These new empires were related, in their external boundaries, to the mediaeval empires and kingdoms, but in administrative structure they were already modern states. It is characteristic that none of the Austrian patrimonial Emperors was crowned and only Ferdinand I received the iron crown as King of Lombardy and Venetia in Milan.

The same transformation is to be seen in the Orders: in place of the binding Orders which originated in the Middle Ages appears the Order of merit, which was first created as such in Austria in 1757, in the form of the military Order of Maria Theresia. The other subsequently created "Orders of the House of Austria" have the same character; in external appearance they are at first still related to the great Orders of the Middle Ages. Soon, however, their costly vestments fell victim to the more modest spirit of the age; in 1838,. at the solemn promotion to the Order of the Iron Crown in the Doge's Palace at Venice, they were worn for the last time.

68   EMPEROR FRANZ I OF AUSTRIA WITH THE AUSTRIAN IMPERIAL MANTLE
   Friedrich von Amerling (born 14th April 1803 in Vienna, died, Vienna, 15th January 1885).
   260 × 164 cm; 102¹/₂ × 64⁵/₈ in. Canvas. Signed: Fr. Amerling, 1832. Picture Gallery. (8618)

69   THE AUSTRIAN IMPERIAL MANTLE
   Made in 1830 to a design of Philipp von Stubenrauch (cf. water-colours No. 71) by Johann Fritz in Vienna.
   Cherry-red velvet with gold embroidery. The principal ornament is the imperial double eagle with the escutcheon. (XIV 117)
   The ermine collar was replaced in 1955, after the original had been destroyed in 1874.
   The mantle was worn in 1830 by Emperor Franz I of Austria on the occasion of the coronation of his son Ferdinand as King of Hungary.

70   DAGGER
   German, beginning of the 17th century.
   115·3 cm; 45³/₈ in. long. Steel with gold inlay; deepened enamel; pearls; rubies. The sheath in red velvet and gilded silver. (XI a 4)
   Under the false assumption that the dagger originally belonged to the Crown of Emperor Rudolph II, the weapon was removed from the Court Hunting and Harness Room and designated as the Austrian imperial sword.

71 FOUR DESIGNS FOR THE MANTLE OF THE EMPEROR OF AUSTRIA
Philipp von Stubenrauch (born 16. 7. 1784 in Vienna, died there 5. 10. 1848).
Water-colour on cardboard.
a) 25·3 × 32 cm; 9⁷/₈ × 12⁵/₈ in. Signed: Stubenrauch 1830. (XIV 42)
b) 32·1 × 22·7 cm; 12³/₄ × 8⁷/₈ in. Signed: Stubenrauch inv. (XVI 40)
c) 33 × 24·6 cm; 13 × 9³/₄ in. Signed: Entwurf von Ph. von Stubenrauch 1831.
  (XVI 41)
Philipp von Stubenrauch was a painter holding the office of Director of
Decorations and Costumes at the Theatres of the Imperial Court.
The cross against b indicates the design approved by the Emperor. As shown
in sheet c, after the coronation of 1830 Stubenrauch once again created a
design for Imperial undergarments. However these garments were probably
never made. In 1830 Emperor Fanz I wore the Hungarian general's uniform
under the Emperor's Mantle. With this mantle the Emperor wore a lighter,
simplified and fashionably altered copy of the Austrian Imperial Crown. In
1871 it was melted down.

72 TABARD AND STAFF OF THE HERALD OF THE AUSTRIAN EMPIRE
*Vienna (?), probably made in 1830, for the same occasion as the mantle of
the Emperor of Austria, i. e. the coronation of Ferdinand I as younger King
of Hungary.*
Gold lamé, velvet, silk. (XIV 55)
The herald's staff carved out of wood, painted and gilded. (XIV 57)

73 EMPEROR FERDINAND I OF AUSTRIA IN THE CORONATION
    VESTMENT OF LOMBARDY AND VENETIA
    A. Weißenböck.
Water-colour (60 × 49 cm; 23³/₄ × 19³/₈ in.). Signed: A. Weißenböck. (XVI 43)
The coronation vestments of Lombardy and Venetia were made for the coronation of Ferdinand I as king of this kingdom (1838 in Milan). In order to
wear the small iron crown of Lombardy, it was necessary to insert it into
a setting of the appropriate size. In the years 1871/72 the Sceptre, Orb and
setting of the crown were broken and sold. Only the objects described as
Nos. 74 and 75 were preserved.

74 THE CORONATION VESTMENT OF THE KINGDOM OF LOMBARDY AND
    VENETIA
    Made in 1838 by Johann Fritz in Vienna to a design of Philipp von Stubenrauch.
The following articles of it are preserved:
a) *Mantle:* Blue velvet with gold embroidery, ermine. On the border the iron
   crown of Lombardy. (XIV 118)
b) *Under-garment:* White moré antique with gold embroidery, lace. (XIV 119)
c) *Sword-belt:* Blue velvet with gold embroidery, the mountings of gilded
   silver. (XIV 120)

75 CORONATION SWORD OF THE KINGDOM OF LOMBARDY AND VENETIA
    *Made in 1838 by Mayerhofer and Klinkosch (hallmark), Vienna, to a design
    by Peter Fendi; the blade by the Viennese steel craftsman Anton Schleifer.*
Gilded silver, blue velvet, steel with etchings and gold inlay. Length 94·1 cm;
37¹/₄ in. (XIV 120)
The blade bears the following inscription: RECTA · TVERI beneath the Austrian
Imperial Crown; on the other side FERDINANDVS · AVSTRIAE · IMPERATOR ·

2*

FRANCISCI · IMP(ERATORIS) · LOMB(ARDIAE) · VENET(IAE) · PRIMI · REGIS · FILIVS · INSIGNI · CORONAE · MEDIOL(ANAE) · MDCCCXXXVIII · SVMPTAE · PRIMVS. Above the inscription the arms of Lombardy and Venetia.

76 TABARD AND STAFF OF THE HERALD OF THE KINGDOM OF LOMBARDY AND VENETIA
Made in 1838 by Johann Fritz in Vienna.
Blue velvet, silver lamé, silk. (XIV 65)
The herald's staff carved out of wood, painted and gilded. (XIV 66)

77 VESTMENT OF A KNIGHT OF THE HUNGARIAN ORDER OF ST. STEPHEN
Vienna, about, or after 1764.
Consists of:
Mantle: green velvet, trimmed with imitation ermine; partly embroidered with gold. On the Collar a Star of the Order.
Under-garment: red velvet, embroidered with gold.
Calpac: red velvet, embroidered with gold, imitation ermine. Livery store. (III/StO-217)

NECK-CHAIN OF THE HUNGARIAN ORDER OF ST. STEPHEN
Vienna, 1836.
Gold, partly enamelled. (XI a 55)
The Order was founded in 1764 by Empress Maria Theresia.

78 VESTMENT OF A KNIGHT OF THE AUSTRIAN ORDER OF ST. LEOPOLD
Vienna, 1808, after a design of Joseph Fischer (Imperial copper-plate engraver and decorator, born 30. 1. 1769 in Vienna, died there 5. 9. 1822).
Consists of:
Mantle: White silk rep trimmed with imitation ermine, partly embroidered with gold. On the border, the heraldic imperial crown. On the collar, Stars of the Orders of St. Leopold and of Maria Theresia.
Coat: light red velvet embroidered with gold.
Hose: light red velvet.
Hat: light red velvet with gold cord.
Sword: (97˙3 cm; 38¹/₂ in. long) and *Sword-belt:* light red velvet, steel, gilded in places.
Livery Store. (III/LO-101)

NECK-CHAIN OF THE AUSTRIAN ORDER OF ST. LEOPOLD
Vienna, 1836.
Gold, enamelled in places. (XI a 55)
The Order was solemnly established on 8th January 1809 by Emperor Franz 1.

79 VESTMENT OF A KNIGHT OF THE AUSTRIAN ORDER OF THE IRON CROWN
Vienna, 1815, after a design of Philipp von Stubenrauch.
Consists of:
Mantle: Violet velvet with silver embroidery. On the border the iron crown and the motto of the Order AVITA ET AVCTA; with orange coloured lining. On the collar a Star of the Order.

Coat: Orange coloured velvet with silver embroidery.
Hat: Violet velvet with silver embroidery.
Sword and Sword-belt: Silver, steel; violet velvet.
Livery store. (III/EK-2)

NECK-CHAIN OF THE AUSTRIAN ORDER OF THE IRON CROWN
Vienna, 1836.

Gold, enamelled in places. (XI a 55)

When the Italian provinces originally belonging to Austria were joined to her again as the Kingdom of Lombardy and Venetia, the Order, founded by Napoleon, was reestablished by Emperor Franz I on 1st January 1816, as an Austrian Order. The emblem of Lombardy, the so-called iron crown, is the symbol of this order.

V. THE TWO INALIENABLE HEIRLOOMS OF THE HOUSE OF HABSBURG

After the death of Emperor Ferdinand I his sons reached an agreement on 11th August 1564 concerning the agate bowl and the "Ainkhürn" (unicorn). These were so supremely valuable to them that they were unwilling to assign them to any one of the heirs as his personal possession. Their agreement lay in the other direction, namely that both pieces should remain the property of the entire House and might not be sold, pledged or taken out of the country. Since that time these two objects have constituted a particularly valuable section of the Treasure chamber.

80 THE AGATE BOWL
Trier, 4th century A. D.

Largest width 75 cm; 29¹/₄ in. Agate (XIV 1)

The bowl is the largest one of its kind. At the bottom there is an inscription, which in the 18th century could still be transcribed as "B. XRISTO · RI · XXPP". It was held to be a miraculous formation of the stone structure. After the 18th century it was, however, no longer legible and only reappeared during a careful cleaning in the year 1951. It dates from the same period as the bowl itself and contains the signature of the artist: Fl(a)b(ius) Aristo Tr(eviris) f(ecit) XX p(ondo). (Reading of University Professor Rudolf Egger, Vienna). No doubt because of the name of Christ, which it was thought could be read, as a result of the false transcription, the bowl was held to be the Holy Grail. Whether it is identical with one of the vessels of that name, which are mentioned in several important mediaeval treasures, cannot be ascertained. Nor can it be proved that the bowl comes from the Burgundian treasure. There are indeed many reports in the 18th century that the bowl was taken as booty by the crusaders at the capture of Constantinople in 1204, and came into Habsburg possession via Charles the Bold and the Burgundian inheritance. The earliest preserved written reference to it dates from 1564.

81 THE "AINKHÜRN" (UNICORN)
Length 243 cm; 95⁷/₈ in. Narwhal horn. (XIV 2)

Such tusks of the narwhal were in earlier times regarded as the horn of the legendary Unicorn, were especially valued on account of this presumed origin, and fetched fantastic sums of money. The Middle Ages saw in the unicorn a symbol of Christ; the legend, according to which the shy animal, fleeing from the pursuing hunters, would only allow itself to be caught by a young virgin, was applied to Christ, who was born of Mary in immaculate virginity.

The horn or "Ainkhürn", as it was called, was thus connected with Christ and signified His victory over death, or more generally, His divine power. It then became thereby a symbol of power and sovereignty as such, and for this reason was often used in insignia. The handle of the sceptre of Andreas Osenbruck (subsequently the Austrian Sceptre; No. 57), and the handle and sheath of the sword of Duke Charles the Bold of Burgundy (No. 148) are made of this material. Prince Bishops often had their crosiers carved from "Ainkhürn" (cf. Ecclesiastical Treasure chamber No. 106). The Renaissance added to the symbolical character of the "Ainkhürn" various healing properties, so that it again became highly valued on this ground. The "Ainkhürn" of the Viennese Treasure chamber is one of the largest. It is a gift from King Sigismund II of Poland to King Ferdinand I, in the year 1540.

82 TAPIS DE VERDURE WITH THE ARMS OF EMPEROR CHARLES V.

Brussels, 2nd quarter of the 16th century (town's mark). Tapestry-maker Willem Pannemaker (Master craftsman's mark).

Tapestries. Gobelins Collection. (XXXIII No. 1, 7, 8)

The double eagle of the Holy Roman Empire is shown with the arms of Emperor Charles V.

VI. JEWELRY COLLECTION

Of the costly jewelry of the Treasure chamber only a few pieces have been preserved, since on 1st November 1918, the Grand Chamberlain of that time, Count Berchtold, took the Imperial private jewelry abroad, acting on the highest order. The most renowned pieces among them were the diamond crown, which was used by Empress Elizabeth on the occasion of the Hungarian Coronation of 1867, and the clasp with the "Florentine", one of the largest diamonds in the world, which Franz Stephan of Lorraine brought with him, together with the treasure of the Grand Dukes of Tuscany, into his marriage with Maria Theresia.

The "Florentine" was the most famous example of a certain group of precious stones which are rarities in every respect on account of their extraordinary size. Some of these pieces were acquired principally because of interest in mineralogy. Whereas insignia and vestments are more directly related to the empire they symbolize, pieces of jewelry and costly decorations of Orders, on the other hand, which are more closely connected with the personality of their wearer, are especially bound up with the remembrance of individual personalities. That Emperor Franz Joseph is only represented by two presentation gifts is characteristic of this soldierly and modest sovereign.

83 COMMEMORATIVE TOKEN OF ALLEGIANCE

Presented to Emperor Franz Joseph I by the Austro-Hungarian army in 1908 in celebration of the 60th year of his reign.

Rudolph Marschall, Vienna (born 1874, still living).

Platinum; diamonds, rubies, enamel. (XI b 64)

84 PRUSSIAN MARSHALL'S BATON
1895.

49 cm; 19³/₈ in. long. Silver; gold; enamel; diamonds, rubies; blue velvet. (XI b 65)

Dedicated to Emperor Franz Joseph by Emperor Wilhelm II of Germany on 17th February 1895. Decorated with the Prussian eagle, the Prussian crown, the monogram and device of Wilhelm and a detailed inscription of dedication.

85 STAR OF THE MILITARY ORDER OF MARIA THERESIA
J. A. Schöll (Frankfurt goldsmith), Vienna 1765.
Silver; gold; rubies; emeralds. Signed: "J. A. Schöll de Franckfurth fait à Vienne ce (!) 20 December 1765." (XI a 16)

86 CROSS OF THE MILITARY ORDER OF MARIA THERESIA
Johann Michael Grosser, Court jeweller, Vienna 1757.
Gold; silver; diamonds; emeralds; rubies. (XI a 17)

87 GREAT CROSS OF THE ORDER OF ST. STEPHEN
Firm of Biedermann, Vienna, 1st half of the 19th century.
Consists of:
a) *Star:* Silver, gold; enamel; diamonds; emeralds.
b) *Cross:* Silver; gold; diamonds; enamel. (XI a 20)

88 CROSS OF THE ORDER OF ST. STEPHEN
Vienna (?), 2nd half of the 18th century.
Silver; gold; enamel; diamonds; rubies; emeralds. (XI a 21)

89 CROSS OF THE ORDER OF ST. STEPHEN
Vienna (?), 1764/65.
Gold; silver; enamel; diamonds; emeralds. (XI a 22)

90 CROSS IN DIAMONDS FOR DISTINGUISHED MILITARY SERVICE
Vienna (?), 1898.
Silver; gold; enamel; diamonds; rubies. (XI a 24)

91 SET OF JEWELRY BELONGING TO ARCHDUCHESS SOPHIE
(Mother of Emperor Franz Joseph I)
2nd third of the 19th century.
Gold; silver; diamonds; emeralds; amethysts. (XVII 31)

92 ONYX CAMEO
Rome (?), 2nd quarter of the 19th century.
Onyx cameo; gold. (XIV 23)
From the possession of Archduchess Sophie.

93 "HUNGARIAN OPAL JEWELRY"
Egger Bros., Budapest 1881.
Enamelled gold; opals; rubies; diamonds. (XI b 41)
Consists of: Girdle, ear pendants, necklace, 10 clasps, 2 bracelets and 5 head pins. Gift of the city Budapest to Princess Stephanie on the occasion of her marriage to Crown Prince Rudolph (10th May 1881).

93 a FOUR BROOCHES OF EMPRESS ELISABETH
Vienna (?), before 1896.
Gold, silver, diamonds, pearls. (XIV 193—196)

93 b BRACELET
From the possessions of Empress Charlotte (1840—1927).
Gold, partly enamelled; diamonds. (XIV 252). Around 1857 (?).

The miniature depicts the Empress's mother, Louise, Queen of the Belgians (painted by Sir William Charles Ross, Court painter of Queen Victoria; 1794 to 1869). On the back of the mounting is the dedication: "Souvenir de la famille. Offert à notre bien aimée Charlotte par ses oncles et ses tantes."

In 1857 Charlotte married Archduke Maximilian Franz, who later became Emperor Maximilian of Mexico.

94 GOLDEN CROSS OF MERIT (CIVIL)
Vienna, 1814.
Gold; an a rep ribbon. (XIV 16)

Founded by Emperor Franz I of Austria for persons who had earned special merit in the defeat of Napoleon in 1813/14, without having been in action. The cross displayed is the one worn by the Emperor himself.

95 NECK-CHAIN OF THE ORDER OF THE GOLDEN FLEECE — FRAGMENT
German, 1st half of the 17th century.
Gold; partly enamelled; rubies; diamonds. (XI a 58)

96 SABRE
Turkish, 2nd half of 17th century. The hilt from the same period but of better quality, did not originally belong to this piece. The mounted silver ornamentations with diamonds are Austrian, around 1712.
91·5 cm; 36¹/₈ in. long. Gold: silver; diamonds; the blade of damask steel; the scabbard of leather. (XI a 50)

The inscriptions on the blade (in English translation): "In the name of God, the kind all-merciful" — "Help from God, Victory and glad tidings for the faithful".

Worn by Emperor Charles VI at his coronation as King of Hungary (22nd May 1712) at Pressburg and by Maria Theresia at her coronation at Pressburg 25th June 1741) and at the Hungarian Diet afterwards.

96 a JEWELRY BOUQUET OF EMPRESS MARIA THERESIA
Johann Michael Grosser, Court jeweller, Vienna, middle of the 18th century.
About 49 cm; 19¹/₄ in. high. Various precious stones; silver; rock crystal.
On loan from the Natural History Museum, mineralogical and petrographical collection.

Gift of Empress Maria Theresia to her husband, Emperor Franz I Stephan, who was a collector of precious stones.

96 b, c TWO FLOWER VASES
Augsburg, end of the 17th century.
24·3 cm; 9⁵/₈ in. and 25·1 cm; 9⁷/₈ in. high. Gilded silver; enamel; precious stones (rubies, emeralds and others). Collections of Sculpture and Handicrafts. (1080 and 1081)

97—104 MEMORIAL PIECES BELONGING TO EMPEROR MAXIMILIAN OF MEXICO
After the execution, in the year 1867, of the Archduke, who was elected Emperor of Mexico on 10th July 1863, these and some other articles (not displayed) in his personal possession were brought to the castle of Miramare and thence to the Treasure chamber.

Mantle and Neck-chain of the Emperor and Grand Master of the Order of Our Blessed Lady of Guadaloupe; (XIV 172, XIV II b)

Neck-chain of the Mexican Order of the Eagle; (XIV II a)

Great Cross of the Royal Greek Order of the Saviour; (XIV II d)

Three Sceptres of the Emperor, of which No. 98 contains the deed concerning his election as Emperor of Mexico and No. 99 a loyal address from the District of Pachua. (XIV 169, 170, 171)

A walking stick. (XIV II e)

105 HYACINTH "LA BELLA"
Set in an Imperial double eagle.
The setting Vienna (?), 1687.
Hyacinth; gold; gilded silver; painted enamel. (XI a 51)

106 HUNGARIAN OPAL
The setting: South German (?), 1st quarter of the 17th century.
Opal; gold, enamelled. (XI a 52)

107 HAIR AMETHYST
The crown shaped settings: Spanish, 17th century.
Amethyst; gold; emeralds. (XI a 53)
Gift of King Charles II of Spain to Emperor Leopold I.

108 TOPAZ
Setting: 2nd half of the 16th century.
Topaz; gold; enamelled. Collections of Sculpture and Handicrafts. (1600)

109 TOPAZ
Setting: 17th century.
Topaz; gold. Collections of Sculpture and Handicrafts. (1904)

110 MILK-WHITE OPAL
Setting: about 1600.
Milk-white opal; gold. Collections of Sculpture and Handicrafts. (1825)

111 AQUAMARINE
Setting: about 1600.
Oriental aquamarine (492 carat); gold. Collections of Sculpture and Handicrafts. (1911)

112 TOPAZ
Setting: 17th century.
Topaz; 2 pearls; gold. Collections of Sculpture and Handicrafts. (1897)

113 GOLDEN ROSE TREE
Giuseppe Spagna (Rome, beginning of the 19th century), 1819.
60 cm; 23³/₄ in. high. Gold. Engraved "GIVS SPAGNA ROMA". (XIV 19)
Yearly, on "Rose Sunday" — i. e. the fourth Sunday in Lent — the Pope consecrates a golden rose tree which he then bestows on someone of high standing, as a special honour. In the year 1819 Pope Pius VII sent this golden rose tree to Empress Carolina Augusta.

113 a THE DIAMOND CROWN OF THE EMPRESS (painting)
Vienna, after 1808.
97 × 93 cm; 38 × 36¹/₂ in. Canvas. (Dept. Prot. 57).
This diamond crown was worn by Empress Maria Theresia already in 1743 for
the entrance at her coronation as Queen of Bohemia and probably also
already in 1741 at her Hungarian coronation. In 1836 before the coronation
of Maria Anna, the wife of Emperor Ferdinand I., the crown was newly
mounted. It remained in that shape in the Viennese Treasure Chamber until
1918. Nothing certain is known concerning its subsequent fate. The painting
shows the crown (front and back) after the coronation of Empress Maria
Ludovica as Queen of Hungary (1808).

VII. MEMENTOES OF THE KING OF ROME
(DUKE OF REICHSTADT) AND OF EMPRESS MARIE LOUISE

On 2nd April 1810, Napoleon Bonaparte, who had himself crowned in 1804 as
Emperor of the French, was married to his second wife Marie Louise, the eldest
daughter of Emperor Franz I of Austria. On 20th March 1811, she gave birth to the
longed for heir to the throne, Napoleon Franz Karl, who received already at birth
the title "King of Rome". After the fall of Napoleon, Marie Louise and her son
went to the court of Vienna. In 1818 Napoleon Franz Karl, who was now called by
his second name, received the lordship of Reichstadt in Bohemia; his Roman Kingdom had become obsolete with the collapse of his father's power. It was in Vienna,
in Schönbrunn Castle, on 22th July 1832, that Franz, Duke of Reichstadt died of
a lung-disease.

114 NAPOLEON BONAPARTE AS KING OF ITALY
Andrea Appiani (born 23. 5. 1754 in Milan, died 8. 11. 1817).
100 × 75 cm; 39¹/₂ × 29⁵/₈ in. Canvas. Monogrammed. Picture Gallery. (2346)
Napoleon is represented in the vestment and with the insignia which he had
ordered for his coronation as King of Italy on 26th May 1805 in Milan; they
were kept in the Viennese Treasure chamber until in 1921 they had to be
given to Italy.
Appiani was the first Italian court painter of Napoleon.

115 MARIE LOUISE, EMPRESS OF THE FRENCH, ARCHDUCHESS OF AUSTRIA
*Paris, Atelier des Gobelins, about or after 1810. Supposedly to a design of
François-Pascal-Simon Gerard.*
82 × 66 cm; 32³/₈ × 26 in. Gobelin. Gobelins collection. (CXIX)

116 NAPOLEON BONAPARTE, EMPEROR OF THE FRENCH
*Jean-Baptiste Isabey (born 11th April 1767, at Nancy, died 18th April 1855
at Paris).*
24·8 × 16·5 cm; 9³/₄ × 6¹/₂ in. Ivory miniature. Signed: ISABEY 1810. (XIV 148)
Counterpart to the miniature of his wife Marie Louise (No. 117). Both originated in the year of Napoleon's marriage with Marie Louise, perhaps on the
occasion of the wedding.

117 MARIE LOUISE, EMPRESS OF THE FRENCH, ARCHDUCHESS OF AUSTRIA
*Jean-Baptiste Isabey (born 11th April 1767 at Nancy, died 18th April 1855
at Paris).*
25·3 × 16 cm; 10 × 6³/₈ in. Ivory miniature. Signed: ISABEY 1810. (XIV 149)
Counterpart to the miniature portrait of Napoleon I. (No. 116)

118 NAPOLEON FRANZ KARL, KING OF ROME, LATER DUKE OF
     REICHSTADT

*Jean-Baptiste Isabey (born 11th April 1767 at Nancy, died 18th April 1855
at Paris).*

15 × 11 cm; 5⁷/₈ × 4³/₈ in. Water colour in wooden frame.

Signed: ISABEY 1815. (XIV 150)

119 THE CRADLE (LE BERCEAU) OF THE KING OF ROME

*Jean-Baptiste Claude Odiot (born 8th June 1763, died 23rd May 1850) and
Pierre Philippe Thomire (born 6th December 1751 at Paris, died there
9th June 1843).*

Silver, gilded; mother of pearl; velvet (stretched over copper plates); silk;
tulle; signed on the two stands respectively: "Odiot et Thomire" and "Thomire
et Odiot".

On the inside of the celestial sphere the inscription: OFFERT PAR LA VILLE
DE PARIS L'AN 1811. (XIV 28)

The design was the work of the painter Pierre Paul Prud'hon (1758—1823).
The cradle is a gift of the city of Paris to Napoleon and his second wife Marie
Louise on the occasion of the birth of their son Napoleon Franz Karl, who
already received at his birth the title "King of Rome". The bed is not an object for everyday use — for which purpose there is a simpler version of the
same design in the Palais of Fontainebleau — but a show-piece, indeed the
"throne bed" of the baby king. It thus stood originally above throne steps and
was covered by a canopy. This concept also explains the generous use of costly
material (it is reported that more than 280 kg of silver were used for it) and
the allegories in the construction of the cradle bed: the cornucopia as symbols
of riches and the genii of Justice and Strength as the supports of the "throne
bed"; over the niche hovers "la Gloire", the Goddess of Fame, the celestial
sphere at her feet. She bears in her hands a laurel wreath on which rests
a wreath of stars with the star of Napoleon. Looking up at this is the eaglet —
the symbol of the King of Rome; "l'aiglon", the little eagle, was his pet name
— which endeavours to spread its wings in order to fly upwards to its father.
On the sides of the bed are two reliefs representing the Seine (Paris) in whose
arms Mercury lays the newly born, and the Tiber (Rome), which observes the
newly risen star. The principal decoration of the cradle centre-piece are the
bees, the symbol of Napoleon, which he substituted for the lily of the Valois
and Bourbons. Their origin were the bees, 300 strong, that were found in the
grave of the Merovingian King Childerich I, when it was discovered in 1653
near Tournai. Emperor Leopold I, who had inherited them after Archduke
Leopold Wilhelm, gave them to King Louis XIV of France. Today only a few
of them are still preserved in the "Cabinet des médailles" at Paris. On the
back of the cradle, the great sovereign arms of Emperor Napoleon I, on the
inner and outer sides of the niche his monogram surrounded by a radiant
wreath.

The festive, colourful impression of the work is today diminished by the almost entirely faded velvet; only in a few places is its original glowing red still
to be seen. Only fragments of the old tulle coverlet have been preserved.

120 TRIPOD WITH BASIN

Manfredini Bros., Milan, 1811.

Silver, gilded; lapis lazuli (mounted on a brass core). Height of the tripod
81·5 cm; 32¹/₂ in. Width of the basin 37 cm; 14⁵/₈ in. (XIV 152)

The tripod is a copy of an antique bronze tripod in the Museo Nazionale at Naples. The basin is decorated with medallions representing water deities; at the centre Neptune and Amphitrite.

Underneath the basin is the signature: INVENTATO ED ESEGVITO DAI FR(ATEL)LI MANFREDINI NELLA R(EGI)A MANIF(ATTV)RA DELLA FONTANA NELL'ANNO 1811. The date was brought into connection with the birth of the King of Rome; the valuable object may thus have been presented to the Imperial pair on this occasion by the city of Milan, in the same way as the cradle was by Paris. The tripod with the basin is probably the only preserved component of a magnificent toilet set of Empress Marie Louise. The decoration of the basin with water deities confirms the use made of the object. The first person to connect the wash basin with the antique forms of a tripod was Jean B. Claude Odiot in 1806.

121 JEWELRY CASKET OF EMPRESS MARIE LOUISE

Martin Guillaume Biennais (known to have worked in Paris from about 1800 to 1832).

Dimensions: 54·7 × 32·2 × 29·5 cm; 21½ × 12¾ × 11⅝ in. Silver, gilded; green velvet; white silk lining. (XIV 153)

The casket is a gift of Napoleon I to his wife Marie Louise. The crowned N, the monogram of the Empress, and the crowned one-headed eagle adorn the corners of the casket; on the lid, the monogram of the Empress.

Signed on the lock: Biennais Orf(èv)re de S(a) M(ajesté) L'Empereur et Roi. The lid of the lock represents the Sovereign arms of Napoleon I.

The small reliefs on the sides of the lid portray the "Aldobrandine Wedding", an antique painting particularly estemed by the Classical Age. They were executed by Augustin Dupré (1748 to 1833), a goldsmith and medallist who was given many commissions, especially by the Napoleonic Court, after already being "graveur général des monnaies françaises" from 1791 to 1803. He often worked together with Biennais as designer and executant of chasing work. The representation of the Aldobrandine Wedding together with the addition of the monograms of Napoleon and Marie Louise leads one to suppose that this was the casket in which the Empress received her wedding present. The principal decorations on the outside of the casket are the evenly arranged bees, the chief symbol of Napoleon (cf. the corresponding note on No. 119). The colour-effect of the casket was originally considerable more intense. Quite apart from the worn gilding of the mountings the virulent green velvet has faded into a moss green.

The little table on which the casket stands today was designed by Theophil Hansen on the occasion of the refurnishing of Hernstein Castle in Lower Austria (1856—1880), from where this piece came to the Treasure chamber together with the tripod (No. 120). The crowned L on the wooden strut refers to the owner of the castle, Leopold Ludwig.

122 MARIA LOUISE, EMPRESS OF THE FRENCH

François-Pascal-Simon Gerard (born 4th May 1770 in Rome, died 11th January 1837 in Paris).

223 × 163·5 cm; 87 × 64 in. Canvas. Picture Gallery. (Dep. Prot. 59)

VIII. THE BURGUNDIAN TREASURE

When the Duchy of Burgundy came back into the posession of the French crown in the year 1361, King John II of the House of Valois enfeoffed in it his younger his rule and that of his successors into a mighty complex of lands, which then, after the death of Duke Charles the Bold in the Battle of Nancy (1477), fell to the Habsson Philip the bold. Trough a skilful policy of marriages the Duchy grew under burgs through the marriage of his daugther Maria with Archduke Maximilian (subsequently Emperor Maximilian I). The Habsburgs thus gained possession of the rich treasure of the Dukes of Burgundy; the still imposing remains of this treasure are preserved in Madrid, Brussels and Vienna. In addition there is kept in Berne and other cities of Switzerland the booty captured by the confederates at the battles of Grandson and Murten. As Dukes of Burgundy the Habsburgs also however now became heads and sovereigns of the Order of the Golden Fleece, which had been founded by Duke Philip the Good in 1429. It thus came about that after the evacuation of Brussels by the Austrian troops, the treasure of the Order which had previously been kept there was consigned to the Treasure chamber in Vienna.

The Order itself is one of the few great chivalrous Orders of the Middle Ages which have maintained themselves in existence until today. The connection with the rich House of the Dukes of Burgundy and with the golden age of Habsburg power has contributed substantially to its special renown. Since the Spanish war of succession there has existed an independet Spanish Order of the Golden Fleece beside the legally established Austrian one.

123 TABARD AND STAFF OF THE HERALD OF THE DUCHY OF BURGUNDY
     (XIV 75/76)
     All the herald's tabard displayed here date either from the 17th century or from the time around 1700 and are worked in velvet, silver and gold rep.
     The mountings of the herald's staffs are of brass.

124 TABARD AND STAFF OF THE HERALD OF THE DUCHY OF BRABANT
     (XIV 79/80)

125 TABARD AND STAFF OF THE HERALD OF THE DUCHY OF LIMBURG
     (XIV 81/82)

126 TABARD AND STAFF OF THE HERALD OF THE DUCHY OF
     LUXEMBOURG
     (XIV 83/84)

127 TABARD AND STAFF OF THE HERALD OF THE COUNTY OF HENNEGAU
     (XIV 85/86)

128 TABARD AND STAFF OF THE HERALD OF THE COUNTY OF FLANDERS
     (XIV 87/88)

130 TABARD AND STAFF OF THE HERALD OF THE COUNTY OF NAMUR
     (XIV 90/91)

131 TABARD AND STAFF OF THE HERALD OF THE COUNTY OF GELDERN
     (XIV 92/93)

133 TABARD OF THE HERALD OF THE COUNTY OF ARTOIS
     (XIV 96)

134 VESTMENT OF A KNIGHT OF THE ORDER OF THE GOLDEN FLEECE
     Vienna, 2nd half of the 18th century.

Consists of:
Mantle: Velvet with gold embroidery, on the border the motto of Duke Charles the Bold of Burgundy "Je l'ay emprins". Lined with white satin.
Under-garment: Velvet.
Hat: Velvet with gold embroidery.
Livery store (III/TO 41)

NECK-CHAIN OF THE ORDER OF THE GOLDEN FLEECE
Vienna, 1836.
Gold, partly enamelled. (XI a 55)

135 TABARD AND STAFF OF THE HERALD OF THE GOLDEN FLEECE
3rd quarter of the 16th century.
Velvet, gold and silver embroidery. Livery store. (III/TO 1)
With the arms of King Philip II of Spain.
Over the tabard the herald wore on festive occasions the "Potence". (No. 145)

136 PHILIP THE BOLD, DUKE OF BURGUNDY (1342—1404)
Copy from the 16th century, after a painting of the 15th century.
36 × 27·2 cm; 14¹/₄ × 10⁷/₈ in. Oil on wood. Picture Gallery. (4443)

137 FEARLESS JOHN, DUKE OF BURGUNDY (1371—1419)
Copy from the 16th century, after a painting of the 15th century.
35 × 28 cm; 14¹/₈ × 11 in. Oil on wood. Picture Gallery. (4443)

138 PHILIP THE GOOD, DUKE OF BURGUNDY (1396—1467)
Copy from the 16th century, after Rogier van der Weyden.
30·8 × 19·5 cm; 12¹/₄ × 7³/₄ in. Oil on wood. Picture Gallery. (4445)

139 CHARLES THE BOLD, DUKE OF BURGUNDY (1433—1477)
Copy from the 16th century, after Rogier van der Weyden.
52·5 × 40·5 cm; 20³/₄ × 16 in. Oil on wood. Picture Gallery. (4425)

140 MARIA, DUCHESS OF BURGUNDY (1458—1482)
Hans Maler (known to have worked from 1500—1510 in Schwaz in Tirol, dated pictures from 1519—1529).
78 × 46 cm; 30⁵/₈ × 18¹/₄ in. Oil on wood. Picture Gallery. (4402)
Maria was the daughter of Duke Charles the Bold; in 1477 she married Archduke Maximilian I, subsequently Elected Emperor.

141 EMPEROR MAXIMILIAN I (1459—1519
Joos von Cleve (active from 1507 onwards, died 1540/41 in Antwerp).
28·5 × 22·3 cm; 11¹/₄ × 8³/₄ in. Oil on wood. Picture Gallery. (972)

142 PHILIP THE FAIR (1478—1506), ARCHDUKE OF AUSTRIA, AFTER 1504 KING OF CASTILLE
Master of the Legend of Magdalene (?) (active about 1490—1530 probably at the court of the Governor, Archduchess Margarethe, at Mecheln).
36 × 25 cm; 14¹/₄ × 9⁷/₈ in. Oil on Wood. Picture Gallery. (3872)

143 VESTMENTS FOR HOLY MASS OF THE ORDER OF THE GOLDEN FLEECE
Burgundian (Brussels?), 2nd and 3rd quarters of the 15th century.
Gold threads; silver threads; silk; velvet; pearls; mock jewels; appliquéd on
linen. Collections for Sculpture and Handicrafts.
Consists of:

a) *Altar antependium.* In the middle, Mary with the Child, who presents to
St. Catharine, kneeling on the right, the ring of the mystic marriage; on the
left John the Baptist. At the side, upper row: prophets and patriarchs;
lower row: apostles. — Inkstand, pen and scroll in Mary's hand indicate
her as the author of the "Magnificat". 330 × 119 cm; 130 × 47 in. (17)

b) *Altar antependium (reredos):* In the middle the stool of grace. At the side,
upper row: prophets and patriarchs; lower row: Apostles. 330 × 120 cm;
130 × 47³/₈ in. (18)

c) *Pluviale ("Cope of Christ").* On the shield, Christ as Judge of the World;
on the orphreys prophets and apostles. In three rows: the archangel Michael
and cherubim; holy martyrs, princes, bishops and doctors. 330 cm; 130 in.
broad, 164 cm; 64¹/₂ in. high. (19)

d) *Pluviale ("Cope of Mary").* On the shield, Mary. On the orphreys: prophets
and apostles. In three rows: the archangel Gabriel with adoring angels;
holy virgins, wives and widows. 330 cm; 130 in. broad, 164 cm; 64¹/₂ in.
high. (21)

e) *Pluviale ("Cope of John").* On the shield, John the Baptist. On the orphreys: prophets and apostles. In three rows: the archangel Raphael with
adoring angels; patriarchs, prophets, holy monks and hermits. 330 cm;
130 in. broad, 164 cm; 64¹/₂ in. high. (20)

f) *Casula (Chasuble).* Over a basic material similar to the pluviale is appliquéd the baptism of Christ, and on the reverse side the transfiguration of
Christ on Mount Tabor. 147 cm; 58 in. long, 131 cm; 51³/₄ in. wide. (14)

g) *Dalmatic.* With representations of female saints; on the orphreys angels.
162 cm; 64 in. long, 128 cm; 50¹/₂ in. wide. (15)

h) *Dalmatic.* With representations of male saints; on the orphreys angels.
154 cm; 60³/₄ in. long, 125 cm; 49¹/₄ in. wide. (16)

A complete set of vestments for a High Mass. The representations on the
shields of the three copes are so arranged that the three priests, who wear
these copes stand next to each other: they portray the ancient representation of the Last Judgment with Christ in the centre as Judge of the world,
flanked on either side by Mary and John the Baptist. It should be added, as
regards the execution of the vestment, that each panel was prepared separately
and inserted in a kind of frame, which is formed by the broad connecting gold
bands. The panels are so worked that in one direction gold threads were
thickly laid and sewn down with the silk threads running vertically. Apart from
the coloured nuances of the silk, the embroiderer thus had a second possibility
of shading: through the close or loose juxtaposition of the silk threads, the
underlying gold threads were brought into play for various effects, whereby
the most delicate passages from one colour to another and a vivid enlivening
of the play of light are achieved. Only the naked bodies and furs are worked
in pure silk embroidery directly on the linen background ("needle painting").
On the two antependia and the chasuble the figures and individual architectural
sections are separately worked and appliquéd on the linen background, so that
in places up to three layers are superimposed. Through this tiering, the dimen-
sional effect is increased; just as by the insertion of genuine precious stones
in the crowns, breast fastenings, etc. the realistic impression is heightened.
The execution of the large vestment is spread over the 2nd and 3rd quarters of

the 15th century. The earliest piece is the antependium (a), the latest the chasuble. One is thus led to assume that several designers were involved, whose respective contributions may not be related to a whole piece of the vestment, but always only with individual panels; the same is true of the hands that did the work. The designer of the earliest pieces is to be sought in the immediate circle of the master of Flemalle (Robert Campin), while the designs of the copes resemble those of his most famous successor, Rogier van der Weyden. In the large scenes of the chasuble, the influence of Hugo van der Goes is apparent.

It is thus perfectly possible that the vestment was begun still in the third decade of the 15th century — i. e. before the founding of the Order of the Golden Fleece, in the inventory of which it is already named in 1477 —, and that the Duke only later donated to his Order the vestment that had already been started. This argument is supported by the fact that, contrary to the usual custom, the emblems of the Order of the Golden Fleece are nowhere to be found, nor Restorations from 17th to 20th century.

144   THE SWEARING-IN CROSS OF THE ORDER OF THE GOLDEN FLEECE
Burgundian, about 1430.

36 cm; 14¹/₄ in. high. Gold; pearls; rubies; sapphires. Loan from the Order of the Golden Fleece. (Dep. Prot. 1)

Behind the front which is partly removable is kept a particle of the Holy Cross. On the stand, the arms and device of Duke Philip the Good of Burgundy, and flint and steel, the emblems of the Order. Before this Cross, the newly nominated knight or officer of the Order had to take the oath.

144 a   CASE FOR THE SWEARING-IN CROSS OF THE ORDER OF THE GOLDEN FLEECE
Burgundian, 2nd quarter of the 15th century.

39 cm; 15³/₈ in. high. Leather, with velvet lining. On the front the coat of arms of the Dukes of the House of Valois. Loan from the Order of the Golden Fleece. (Dep. Prot. 2)

145   THE "POTENCE" (CHAIN OF ARMS) OF THE HERALD OF THE ORDER OF THE GOLDEN FLEECE
Netherlands (Flemish?), after 1517.

Circumference outside 143 cm; 56³/₈ in., inside 98·8 cm; 39 in.

Height of a plaque plus chain 11 cm; 4³/₈ in. Gold, partly enamelled. Loan of the Order of the Golden Fleece. (Dep. Prot. 4)

Consists of a neck-chain of the Order and a Collar with 26 plaques in each of which 2 small armorial shields are inserted. Each of these shields bears the arms of a knight of the Order. Two places (in the middle of the front) are reserved for the sovereign. Thus is composed the total of 51 knights of the Order, as laid down by Emperor Charles V.

The armorial plaques are interchangeable, so that all living members of the Order could be represented on the Potence. However it seems that this usage was not regularly practised. The plaques date from widely varying periods: from the early 16th to the end of the 17th century. The Potence replaces an older, similar herald's chain with 32 plaques corresponding to the original maximum number of 31 knights.

146   SIX ARMORIAL PLAQUES FOR THE POTENCE
Gold, partly enamelled. Loan of the Order of the Golden Fleece. (Dep. Prot. 5)

147 THE BURGUNDIAN COURT GOBLET
Burgundian, about 1425—1450.
46 cm; 18¹/₄ in. high. Rock crystal; gold, partly enamelled; pearls; diamonds; rubies. Collections for Sculpture and Handicrafts. (27)
From the possessions of Duke Philip the Good.

148 THE "AINKHÜRN" (UNICORN) SWORD
Burgundian, 2nd half of 15th century.
106 cm; 41³/₄ in. long. Steel; "Ainkhürn" (narwhal horn); gold; gold enamel; gilded silver; one ruby; pearls. (XIV 3)
From the possessions of Duke Charles the Bold.

149 RING
Burgundian, 2nd half of 15th century.
Gold, set with diamonds. Collections for Sculpture and Handicrafts. (131)
The diamonds form an M. On the shoulders of the ring the letters C H I, no doubt the abbreviation of the name Jesus written backwards. According to tradition the engagement ring of Duchess Maria of Burgundy.

150 BROOCH
Netherlands, 1430—1440.
5 cm; 1⁷/₈ in. wide. Gold, partly enamelled; set with pearls and precious stones. Collections for Sculpture and Handicrafts. (130)
Shows a betrothed couple (or pair of lovers) in a garden.

151 THREE BREAST FASTENINGS FOR THE COPES OF THE MASS VESTMENTS
Burgundian, around 1500. Vienna (?), beginning of 19th century.
19 cm; 7¹/₂ in. high. Gilded silver, partly enamelled. Loan of the Order of the Golden Fleece.
The arms are those of Archduke Philip the Fair. At the beginning of the 19th century, the damaged armorial shield with the Archduke's hat was replaced by copies.

IX. THE INSIGNIA AND REGALIA OF THE HOLY ROMAN EMPIRE

The tokens of sovereignty, coronation vestments and relics collected here were merged in the course of the Middle Ages into one treasure, which to that epoch signified more than simply magnificent craftmanship that served to heighten royal splendour.

These objects were the security, the seal of sovereignty. The Holy Roman Empire was an elective empire and its rulers proved their legality not through right of succession, but through the possession of the insignia, handed down through the ages. It is understandable, therefore, that the kings of that empire not seldom incurred great sacrifice in order to gain possession of them, and that conversely their possession could influence the election.

Again, the old imperial relics were intended to designate the ruler as the legal representative of Christ. For the Supreme Sovereign of the Empire was indeed Christ. Through His act of redemption He assured His rights of Sovereignty over the world.

which should submit to His "Imperium", in fact the Holy Roman Empire. Only in the late Middle Ages was this lofty significance of the imperial relics forgotten, and in its place appears a zealous collecting and studying of relics, intended to benefit and bless the pious individual. In this way, the "instructions in sacred objects" came about, at which the Imperial treasure was displayed with solemn ceremony to the assembled crowd. Under the influence of this attitude the insignia and vestments also came to be regarded as relics, as they were connected with the figure of Charlemagne, first occidental Emperor who was canonized. The last "instruction in sacred objects" took place in 1523. Then Nürnberg, where the Imperial treasure was kept at this time, went over to the Reformation.

During these developments the original concept of the Empire became progressively more restricted, so that in the course of time the Holy Roman Empire became a national Empire and for that reason was called, from the 15th century onwards, the "Holy Roman Empire of the German Nation".

The Holy Roman Empire began with the coronation of Charlemagne on Christmas Day of the year 800, and was declared dissolved by Emperor Franz II (The Austrian Emperor Franz I) in 1806, under the pressure of Napoleonic victories.

The insignia of the Empire were originally kept personally by the ruling Emperor or King. They were partly kept by the ruler with him, and partly deposited in strong castles (Trifels, Kyburg, etc.). After 1424, the free imperial city of Nürnberg kept the Imperial Treasure, which was subsequently placed at the ruler's disposal only for his coronation. It was removed in 1796 before the advancing French, and finally in the year 1800 deposited in the Vienna Treasure chamber.

Here the insignia were united with the regalia that until then had always been kept in Aachen Cathedral. Legend says that these regalia were found in the grave of Charlemagne: the Imperial Book of Gospels, the burse of St. Stephen and the sabre of Charlemagne (Nos. 160—162). In the years 1938—1945, the Insignia of the Empire were again kept at Nürnberg.

152 THE IMPERIAL CROWN

West German, 2nd half of 10th century (962), with later additions.

Height of the front slab 15·6 cm; 6¹/₈ in.; height of the cross 9·9 cm; 3⁷/₈ in. Gold, gold filigree; various precious stones; pearls; enamel. (XIII 1)

The crown was earlier thought to be that of the Burgundian Empire, which at its accession to the Empire in 1033, would be elevated to the dignity of Imperial crown, or else as a gift of Pope Benedict VIII to Emperor Henry II; its place of origin was sought in Burgundy, Fulda or Mainz. Today it is considered that the crown was made in a German goldsmith's workshop for the Imperial coronation of Otto the Great in 962, in Rome. It had always had only one arch, although the arch preserved to-day is from the time of Emperor Konrad II (1024—1039). The cross probably dates from late in the reign of Otto III, or from the early part of the reign of Henry II, and replaces the covers which originally consisted of pearls, the empty sockets of which are still preserved on the two temple-plates and the neck-plate.

The pendilia, the sockets of which can be seen on the lower side of the temple-plates, have not been preserved.

The top stone of the brow-plate is an addition of the 14th century. Originally, the famous "stone of wisdom", referred to by, among others, Walther von der Vogelweide, was set here; it was last mentioned in 1350. The hyacinth in the middle row of the neck-plate is also an addition, this time from the late 18th century. The red velvet mitre inside the crown is probably from the 18th century.

The eight plates are graded in size according to their importance; the four main plates above the brow, the neck and the temples are adorned only with precious stones; while the four intervening plates contain enamel plaques.

These represent: Christ as Lord of the Universe; Isaiah prophesies to the sick King Ezechias that God gives him another 15 years of life; King David as the symbol of justice and King Solomon as the symbol of wisdom. The mottos added are quotations from the coronation service and indicate the basic principles of a happy government: the Emperor is the representative of Christ, the Pantokrat (humility); long life; justice; fear of God (wisdom). The most important part of the crown is, however, the main plates with their ornamentation of precious stones, whose domination was always characteristic of the crown of the sovereign ruler. Rightly, a plan is sought which represents a connection between the Old and New Testaments (High priests — Apocalypse with the Divine Empire of Christ). The octagonal outline of the crown is also symbolical; eight as a figure of perfection frequently occurs in works of art related to the Empire.

The shape of the crown is derived from two forms of imperial head-dress of late antiquity: the laurel wreath and the imperial helmet. From the former is derived the circlet (octagonal), from the latter the arch has been preserved.

153 THE IMPERIAL ORB

West German (Cologne?), last quarter of the 12th century.

21 cm; $8^{1}/_{4}$ in. high. Gold, gold filigree, precious stones and pearls. (XIII 2)

The sphere consists of a resinous mass covered with gold foil. The row of pearls belonging to the equatorial girdle and the cross (side) have been lost. At the point where the arms of the cross intersect there is an intaglio — a sapphire — with the lower side turned outwards, which bears a sign so far unexplained, resembling the monograms of the Merovingian kings.

The Imperial Orb — actually the sphere of the universe — is one of the oldest symbols of all embracing power. The Christian Empire set the cross on its pole. In the coronation ceremonial, the Imperial Orb first appears in 1191, although judging from pictures the earlier Middle Ages also knew the Imperial Orb as a symbol of sovereignty.

154 THE SCEPTRE

German, 1st half of the 14th century.

61.5 cm; $24^{1}/_{2}$ in. long. Gilded silver. (XIII 3)

155 THE IMPERIAL SWORD (MAURITIAN SWORD)

The sword: German, about 1198—1218;

The scabbard: German, 1st half of the 11th century.

110 cm; $43^{3}/_{8}$ in. long. Steel; pommel and cross-bar slightly gilded; the hilt bound with silver wire. The scabbard of olive wood, covered with gold foil, enamel plates, at the edges garnets; the rows of pearls which outlined the separate panels have been lost. (XIII 17)

The pommel of the sword bears the inscription BENEDICTVS DO(MINV)S DE(V)S · QVI · DOCET MANVS and the Imperial eagle or arms of King Otto IV (of Brunswick). From the same craftsman come the inscriptions on the cross-bar: † CRIST(V)S : VINCIT : CRISTVS REINAT and CRISTVS VINCIT : CRISTVS REIGNAT : CRIST(V)S INPERAT. The blade, repeatedly sharpened, shows as mark a cross potent in a circle. The silver wire of the hilt is probably an addition of the 16th or 17th century.

The scabbard is covered with 14 plaques in gold foil, each of which shows a frontal sovereign figure enchased. It is thought the 14 figures were intended to represent a specific line of rulers. It follows that the scabbard was made for Henry III. Of course precisely the number 14 (2×7) suggests the possibility of symbolical intentions. Between the plaques of gold foil are little enamel plates which were partly restored in the 17th and 18th centuries. A panel with wire enamel on a green background is a Viennese addition from the beginning of the 20th century. This late addition is explained by the fact that the Mauritian sword was the only article of the Insignia of the Empire still to be used by the Austrian Emperor at special ceremonies, the last of which was the coronation of the Austrian Emperor Charles as King of Hungary in 1916.

The sword was intended principally for ceremonial carrying with the point upwards: it was carried thus in solemn procession by the sword-bearer proceding the sovereign. The verse in praise of Christ on the cross-bar is the end of the "Laudes", the solemn hymns of homage to the newly crowned ruler.

156 THE IMPERIAL CROSS

West German, about 1024.

77 cm; 30³/₈ in. high. Oak, mounted with thin gold foil. On the front precious stones; on the side walls and the back niello work. (XIII 21)

The original shrine of the Imperial relics. On the front, several parts can be moved away from the opening where the relics were kept: in the crossbeam the Holy Lance (No. 157), in the shaft the particles of the Holy Cross (No. 158). The niello work on the back shows eleven apostles grouped around the apocalyptic lamb, and the four symbols of the evangelists. On the side-walls is the running inscription: ECCE : CRVCEM : DOMINI : FVGIAT : PARS : HOSTIS : INIQVI : HINC : CHVONRADE : TIBI : CEDANT : OMNES : INIMICI. The name applies to Konrad II who was therefore thought to be the founder. The text is not, however an inscription of dedication, so that Konrad may be thought of as completing the Imperial Cross but not necessarily as founding it. The cross seems to have been ordered by Emperor Henry II, but was not finished until under his successor Konrad II.

The stand of today (17·3 cm; 6³/₄ in. high, gilded silver over wood), was made in 1352 by order of Emperor Charles IV. Two of the four armorial shields show the one-headed Imperial eagle, looking to the right, the other two the Bohemian lion. The inscription runs: ANNO MILLENO TERCIO QVINQVAGENO SECVNDO KAROLVS AVGVSTVS ROMANVS REXQVE BOHEMVS HOC LIGNVM DOMINI PEDE SIC DECORAVIT.

157 THE HOLY LANCE

Langobardian (?).

51 cm; 20¹/₈ in. long, steel; iron; silver; gold; leather. (XIII 19)

A pointed oval part is missing from the lance's blade and is filled in with an iron nail hammered into ornamental form — the Holy Nail. The lowest third of this piece of iron is missing. The lance's blade is broken and kept together by a small iron band. Above this band there is a broader, silver one, which bears, against a golden background, the following words: CLAVVS DOMINICVS † HEINRICVS D(E)I GR(ATI)A TERCIVS ROMANO(RVM) IMPERATOR AVG(VSTVS) HOC ARGENTVM IVSSIT FABRICARI AD CONFIPMATIONE(M) CLAVI D(OMI)NI ET LANCEE SANCTI MAVRITII SANCTVS MAVRITIVS. All this is covered by another golden band with the inscription: † LANCEA ET CLAVVS DOMINI. On the lower part two blade-like flanges are inserted in folds, they may have been made of the steel saved from the place where the nail is inserted. The flanges and the Holy Nail are tied to the lance's blade by silver wire, the first also by thin leather straps. Into these parts of the Holy Lance and the thick parts of the Holy Nail crosses are inserted, framed by a gold alloy. Apart from that the

Holy Lance was a relic specially precious for the Holy Nail. In decisive battles it was carried against the enemy as insignia of the king, and different victories were attributed to its power (Victory on the Lech, 955).

King Rudolf of Burgundy acquired it from the Upper-Italian Count Samson as an insignia of the regnum Italicum. King Rudolf passed it on to Henry I (probably 935 in Ivois, Carignan). Indirectly it was a prerequisite to achieve imperial dignity, because only the King of Italy could also become Emperor. Since Konrad II, the Holy Lance was venerated as lance of Saint Mauritius, and after the early 13th century as the lance with which Longinus pierced the side of Our Lord.

The Holy Lance was originally placed in the crossbeam of the Imperial Cross (No. 156). Only when carried in procession in front of the ruler, was it mounted on a shaft, covered by a precious sheath, on which probably the particle of the Holy Cross (No. 158) was fixed. The inner silver band of the Holy Lance was added by Henry IV, the outer golden one by Charles IV. It is likely that Charles IV also had the lowest third of the nail broken off; perhaps the reliquary of the cross's nail was made for it and then given to the Cathedral's treasure.

158 THE RELIQUARY WITH THE PARTICLE OF THE CROSS

German, 14th century.

31 cm; 12¼ in. high. Gold. (XIII 20)

The particle of the cross, which had its place originally in the lower shaft of the Imperial Cross, is, besides the Holy Lance the oldest and most dignified Imperial relic. The prosaic setting in form of a processional Cross showing the Cross's span uncovered as widely as possible seems to belong to the time Charles IV.

159 THE ASPERGILLUM (SPRINKLER)

German, late 13th or early 14th century.

58·5 cm; 23¼ in. high. Silver. (XIII 4)

160 THE IMPERIAL BOOK OF GOSPELS

So-called Palace-School, Aachen, end of the 8th century.

Manuscript: Measurements of silk 324 × 249 mm; 12¾ × 9⅞ in. Purple coloured parchment, gold, silver.

Cover: 345 × 261 mm; 13⅝ × 10¼ in. Red velvet, mountings and lid in gilded silver; Hans von Reutlingen, Aachen, about 1500 (goldsmith's mark R₃ 30, town's mark R₃ 13). (XIII 18)

The manuscript consists of 236 purple coloured pages of parchment. On it the texts are written in gold and silver, in uncial writing and capitalis rustica. The canon plates are divided by painted imitation-antique architectures. The beginnings of the gospels are decorated by illuminated initials, which in their ornamental style resemble Irish-Anglo-Saxon models. Before the beginnings of the Gospel are miniatures with representations of the evangelists. The Imperial Book of Gospels, together with three other manuscripts at Aachen, Brussels and Berlin, belongs to a writing-school, described as the "School of the Palace" (of Charlemagne), which earlier was connected with Rheims, now rather with Aachen. Previously, the "DEMETRIVS PRE" in the marginalia on folio 118 recto was interpreted as the name of the writer. But the place is unusual for a signature, and one is now inclined to look for it in the erasure on folio 235 at the end of the book.

The lid of the cover of Hans von Reutlingen represents God the Father on the throne, as prototype and ideal of all rulers, vested with imperial robes and a crown, which is thought to be the private crown of the Emperors Frederick III or Maximilian I. The features of God the father seem to be like an ideal picture of Charlemagne, who was regarded as a paragon by all Emperors of the Holy Roman Empire. Around God the Father is represented the Annunciation to Mary and the symbols of the four evangelists. At the coronation, the king to be crowned took the oath on this Book, his fingers raised in the act and touching the page at the beginning of the Gospel of St. John.

161 THE BURSE OF ST. STEPHEN

Rheims (?), 1st third of the 9th century.

32 cm; 12⁵/₈ in. high. Gold foil on wood; the back gilded silver; precious stones; pearls. (XIII 26)

A reliquary which according to tradition contained earth soaked with the blood of the arch-martyr Stephen. The wooden core does in fact contain cavities, in which relics must have lain; they are however empty except for one compartment at the bottom of the reliquary. There lies a relic which cannot be more closely identified, a white fragment of cloth wrapped in a yellow-brown piece of sheet and authenticated by a seal of the Cathedral Chapter of Worms dating from the 1st half of the 12th century.

The sides show stamped medallions with the often recurring representations of a goddess of Vengeance (inscription: MALIS VINDICTA), of a fisherman, of a falconer and a bird-trapper. In style they are connected with the so-called "Psalter of Utrecht" which originated in the first third of the 9th century, probably in Rheims. The back was originally adorned in the same way as the side walls; in the empire period it was replaced — perhaps on the occasion of the exhibition of the Insignia of the Empire in the year 1827 in Vienna — by the present cover which in its formation essentially follows the old. The four trapeze-shaped panels and the two square ones above and below the large centre medallion indicate the now empty relic boxes of the wood. The crowning of the reliquary was probably added in the 15th century.

162 THE SABRE OF CHARLEMAGNE

Eastern Europe (Hungary?), 2nd half of the 9th century, or 10th century.

90·5 cm; 35³/₄ in. long. Handle: wood, fish skin, gold, gilded silver, precious stones. Blade: steel, gilded copper inlay. Sheath, 86·5 cm; 34¹/₈ in. long: wood, leather, gold mountings. (XIII 5)

The sabre was earlier considered to be a present of Harun al Raschid to Charlemagne, or else a piece of the booty won by Charlemagne from the Avars. The wood of the hilt covered with fish skin burst, whereupon it was bound round, probably still in the 14th or 15th century, with the three bands of gilded silver partly set with precious stones.

The sheath is made of wood (probably renewed), which is covered with more recent leather and partly with more recent gold foil. Probably the only old elements are the three ornamental mountings.

With this sabre the kings were girt at the coronation by the Archbishop of Cologne.

163 THE CORONATION MANTLE

Palermo, Royal workshop, 1133/34.

342 cm; 136 in. broad. Scarlet silk, richly embroidered with gold. The scenes portrayed were outlined in dark blue silk and double rows of pearls; the blue

threads however have largely dropped out. Little gold enamel plaques, two clasps with enamel, vermicule filigree work and precious stones; two mantle fastenings with filigree work and three rubies. The mantle is lined with a gay Italian damask richly worked with gold and silver, that was probably added on the occasion of the coronation of King Charles V (1520) in the nunnery of St. Clare at Nürnberg.

Underneath is still the old lining, consisting of parts: 1. a silk material with green tendrils and golden flowers on a brown background, covering most of the area of the coat; 2. following the straight border, five pieces of the three gold brocades are sewn on, in a width of 20·5 to 37 cm; $8^{1}/_8$ to $14^{5}/_8$ in.; these were prepared in Palermo at the same time as the mantle, and are termed the Fall cloth (I), Dragon cloth (II) and Bird cloth (III). Their patterns have not so far been satisfactorily explained. (XIII 14)

On the border of the mantle is a cufic inscription which in translation reads: "(this mantle) belongs to the articles worked in the Royal workshop, in which fortune and honour, prosperity and perfection, merit and distinction have their home. May the king rejoice in good acceptance, thriving magnificently, in great generosity and high splendour, renown and magnificence and the fulfilment of wishes and hopes; may his days and nights be spent in enjoyment, without end or change; in the feeling of honour, dependency and active participation in happiness and in the maintenance of well-being, support and suitable activity; in the capital of Sicily in the year 528 (the Hedschra)". The surface of the mantle shows two stylized lions, each attacking a camel; between them arises the tree of life. According to the inscription, this mantle was made in the years 1133/34 for King Roger II. It is the oldest and most significant piece of the unique treasure of vestments which the Norman kings ordered for themselves in Sicily, which then passed to the Swabians, and from which a few selected pieces were incorporated into the Imperial treasure probably following the coronation of the Emperor Frederick II in Rome (1220).

The apparel of the Emperor at the coronation is modelled on that of a bishop: over the Alb (No. 165) he wears the tunicella (No. 164), over which lies the stole (No. 173). The mantle is worn on top of that. The vestment is completed by pontifical hose, shoes and gloves (Nos. 167—169).

164 THE DALMATIC (TUNICELLA)

Palermo, Royal workshop, about 1130—1154.

141 cm; $55^{5}/_8$ in. high. Deep purple coloured silk, the trimmings of a scarlet silk similar to the Coronation Mantle; little gold tubes; gold plates with enamel and vermicule filigree work; gold lace; pearl trimmings. (XIII 6)

Perhaps from the same vestment as the Coronation Mantle. As the Dalmatic is smaller and narrower than the Alb from the Insignia of the Empire, at later coronations the reverse order of dressing was observed, namely first the Dalmatic, and above the Alba, if one did not take the considerably bigger and wider Imperial Eagle-Dalmatic (No. 166) instead of the Sicilian one.

165 THE ALB

Palermo, Royal workshop, 1181, with later additions.

157 cm; 62 in. high. Yellowish taffeta on silk of the same colour; trimmings with rich gold embroidery and pearls, gold lace; precious stones. (XIII 7)

Two similar inscriptions on the lower orphrey, one in Latin, one in Arabic running band, say that the Alb was made in the Royal workshop in Palermo for King William II in 1181. The design on the orphrey consists of adverse lions on white, and adverse gryphons on a purple background. The orphreys on the sleeves are similar, but pieces have been added at the time of the Swabian kings; the breast trimming is of the same scarlet silk. The taffeta of the Alb was renewed already for the coronation of Charles V (1520), the one of today is probably even more recent.

166 THE EAGLE DALMATIC

Chinese cloth, around 1300. orphreys and medallions South German, 1st half of 14th century.

160 cm; 63 in. high. Purple coloured Chinese damask with medallions sewn on with eagles in black silk embroidery, the eagles eyes of enamel; the orphreys gold and silk. (XIII 15)

First mentioned in 1350. It is not known whether it was occasionally used at coronations instead of the Sicilian dalmatica; in any case, Dürer, in his idealized portrait of Charlemagne, represents the Emperor as wearing the eagle dalmatic. It can also not yet be judged whether, and to what extent, the likenesses of princes on the orphreys are intended to represent a specific line of rulers; the bust portraits on the neck orphrey which differ somewhat from the others may perhaps represent Virtues. A cowl belonging to the eagle dalmatic was lost when the Insignia of the Empire were hastily transferred from Nürnberg.

167 THE GLOVES

Sicily, beginning of the 13th century (before 1220).

Circumference of the openings 24 and 25 cm; 9³/₈ and 9³/₄ in. Length (opening to middle finger tip): 25·5 and 27 cm; 10 and 10⁵/₈ in. Scarlet silk with gold embroidery; pearls; rubies; sapphires; little gold enamel plaques. (XIII 11)

The gold embroidery on each palm forms a one-headed eagle looking left; the little gold enamel plaques on the outside show sirens, palmettes, heads of eagles and so-called "Norman shields" (which might be interpreted, together with the eagle's heads, as abbreviated eagles). The little plaque with half-length portrait of an angel is a German addition of the 14th century.

168 THE HOSE

Sicily, about 1154—1169.

Circumference of the openings 40 and 41 cm; 15³/₄ and 16¹/₄ in.; length (opening to heel): 60 and 60·5 cm; 23³/₄ and 23⁷/₈ in. Red silk, gold embroidery. The border in green silk. (XIII 12)

On the border a partly preserved inscription: "For the highly honoured, hallowed King William, who may be honoured through God, helped through His omnipotence . . .". This might be intended for King William I or William II. Restored with light green silk by the Nuns of St. Clare at Nürnberg 1520, before the coronation of Charles V.

169 THE SHOES

Sicily, 1st quarter of the 13th century.

Lengths of the soles 25·5 and 26 cm; 10 and 10¹/₈ in. Red silk; pearls; rubies, amethysts; one emerald; gold border with sirens and gryphons; red and green framed; sole of neat's leather. (XIII 13)

170 THE BELT FOR THE SWORD OF ST. MAURITIUS

Sicily, probably beginning of the 13th century, the mountings perhaps German, 13th/14th century.

190 cm; 75 in. long, 6·3 cm; 2¹/₂ in. wide. Gold border with palmettos, in white, green and red silk; mountings in gilded silver. (XIII 9)

On the border of the belt the inscription: CRISTVS RIEHGNAT CRISTVS INQPARAT DDEVS.

171 THE GIRDLE ("CINGULUM PONTIFICALE")

Sicily, probably the 12th century.

150 cm; 59 in. long, 3·5—3·8 cm; $1^3/_8$—$1^1/_2$ in. wide. Blue silk studded with pearls, rubies on little plaques in gold filigree; the border hemmed with red silk and gold threads. (XIII 10)

The girdle was used to tie around the Alb.

172 THE CEREMONIAL SWORD

Sicilian, before 1220.

108·5 cm; $42^1/_2$ in. long. Hilt and cross-bar of wood, covered with gold plaques decorated with filigree and enamel; the teel blade, many times ground off, bears as emblem a cross-potent; the pommel of gilded silver with the one-headed Imperial Eagle and the Bohemian lion dates from the time of Charles IV. Sheath (92·5 cm; $36^1/_2$ in. long) of linen, the outside thickly covered with gilded silver threads; over that are gold plaques with enamel and vermicule filigree; pearls, four rubies; inside a wooden sheath covered with parchment. (XIII 16)

Together with the gloves and cap of the crown which was placed in the grave in Palermo of Empress Constance, the ceremonial sword forms one set which was prepared for Emperor Frederick II. He wore it for his coronation in Rome in the year 1220.

After the coronation in later times the emissaries of Nürnberg were knighted with the sword.

173 THE STOLE

Middle- or South Italy (?), 14th century (before 1338).

585·5 cm; 231 in. long, 20—23·5 cm; $7^3/_4$—$9^1/_4$ in. wide. Yellow silk with gold design (eight pieces joined), eagles embroidered on with black silk, the stylized clasps in gold with deepened enamel and granulation; clasps, medallions and borders studded with double rows of pearls; scarlet linen lining with white silk borders studded with double rows of pearls; scarlet linen lining with white silk ribbon from the 18th century sewn on. (XIII 8)

It imitates the "lorum", the sash of the Byzantine ruler; the Roman Emperors did not however wear it as they did in complicated folds, but as the Roman clerics, laid around the neck and crossed over the breast.

174 THE RELIQUARY WITH THE TOOTH OF JOHN THE BAPTIST

German, 14th century.

41 cm; $16^1/_4$ in. high, gilded silver, rock crystal. (XIII 27)

On the strip of parchment lying in the reliquary is the inscription: "Dens de mento s(ancti) Joh(ann)is Baptiste su(m)ptus in Taurino."

175 THE RELIQUARY WITH THE ARM BONE OF SAINT ANNE

Prague (?), 3rd quarter of the 14th century (?).

$21 \times 3·5 \times 3·5$ cm; $8^1/_4 \times 1^3/_8 \times 1^3/_8$ in. Gold; gilded silver. (XIII 28)

The oldest inventory of the Insignia of the Empire of 1246, names among the relics an arm-bone of St. Kunigund, the wife of Emperor Henry II. In the inventory of 1350 this is missing, but the arm-bone of St. Anne appears instead. It is probably one and the same relic, which comes from St. Kunigund, and its name was changed between 1246 and 1350. On the binding is the inscription: † ISTVD EST BRA(CH)IV(M) S(AN)C(T)E ANNE M(AT)RIS B(EA)TE MARIE.

176   THE RELIQUARY WITH THE PIECE OF WOOD FROM CHRIST'S CRADLE
      Prague, between 1368 and 1378.
      49 × 4·1 × 2·1 cm; 19³/₈ × 1⁵/₈ × ⁶/₈ in. Gold; precious stones; pearls. (XIII 24)
      The relic was given by Pope Urban V in 1368 to Emperor Charles IV, who had
      the case made for it. In the middle of the lid is a small window through
      which, when opened, one sees a silhouette of the cradle, and underneath the
      piece of wood. The outside stone on the right is an antique intaglio with the
      representation of a sea-nymph on a sea-horse and the signature: ΘΑΜΥΡΟΥ.

177   THE RELIQUARY WITH A PIECE OF THE ROBE OF JOHN THE
      EVANGELIST
      Prague, around 1368—1378.
      24·8 × 15 × 1·3 cm; 9³/₄ × 5⁷/₈ × ¹/₂ in. Gold with niello inlay. (XIII 25)
      The relic, a piece of plain silk, was given to Emperor Charles IV, by Pope
      Urban V in 1368. The Emperor had the reliquary made in the same workshop
      in which the casket for the links of the chains (No. 178) were made.
      On the lid of the casket are eight scenes from the life of St. John the Evan-
      gelist, in niello work: Christ speaks to Salome, the mother of James and John;
      the Last Supper; John is martyred in a cauldron of boiling oil in the reign of
      Emperor Domitian; the heathen priest Aristodemus hands St. John the poison
      which has killed three miscreants; St. John restores these three to life; the
      landing of the Saint on Patmos; John reveals his visions to his disciples; his
      burial. In the centre of the lid a cruciform aperture, closed by means of a
      rockcrystal plaque, gives a view of the relic. Above the cross is a small, late
      antique cameo with one eagle (used here again as symbol of the Evangelist).
      On the front of the casket the explanatory inscription: de · tunica · s(ancti) ·
      iohannis · ewa(n)gel(iste).

178   THE RELIQUARY WITH CHAIN-LINKS
      Prague, about 1368—1378.
      12·5 × 4·7 × 2·8 cm; 9⁷/₈ × 1⁷/₈ × 1¹/₈ in. Gold with niello inlay. (XIII 29)
      The three chain-links are supposed to be parts of the iron chains with which
      the apostles John the Evangelist, Peter and Paul were bound in prison. They
      were given to Emperor Charles IV by Pope Urban V in 1368. Each link is
      fastened to a small gold chain, bearing a gold plaque with the designation of
      the relic, and a ring. The rings on the links of St. Paul and St. John come from
      the same workshop. They have red and blue enamel inlays with the inscription
      IEXVS AVTEM TRANSIENS PER M(ARE) and each bears a stone; the first one
      a late Roman intaglio with the head of Antoninus Pius, the last one a
      Byzantine cameo portraying Mary with hands raised in prayer. The rings them-
      selves are Italian work of the 14th century. On the link of St. Peter hangs a
      simple gold band with a small disc engraved with the head of St. Peter
      (14th century).
      On the lid of the casket are portrayed the three chained Apostles, and on the
      front, the gift of the links to Emperor Charles IV by Pope Urban V. From the
      same workshop certainly comes the reliquary with the piece of the robe of
      St. John the Evangelist (No. 177) and a reliquary in the treasure of Prague
      Cathedral with a piece of the loin cloth of Christ.

179   THE RELIQUARY WITH A PIECE OF THE TABLE CLOTH OF CHRIST
      Hans Krug the Younger, Nürnberg, 1518.
      55 cm. 22 in. high. Gilded silver; pearls; precious stones. Town-mark of Nürn-
      berg R₃ 3736. (XIII 22)

Inside the foot an inscription with the names of the persons who ordered the reliquary. They are the men who, by order of the City of Nürnberg, had to administer the Insignia of the Empire. As "guards of the shrine", the Saints of the town St. Sebald and St. Lorenz. On the back of the little box an engraving of the Last Supper, of which table cloth the relic is thought to have come. But the embroidery is from the 13th century at the earliest.

Counterpart to No. 180.

180 THE RELIQUARY WITH A PIECE OF THE APRON OF CHRIST
Hans Krug the Younger, Nürnberg, 1518.
55 cm; 21³/₄ in. high. Gilded silver, pearls, precious stones.
Town-mark of Nürnberg R₃ 3736. (XIII 23)
On the back an engraving of the washing of feet; the relic is said to come from the apron Christ used.
Counterpart to No. 179, with a similar inscription in the inside of the foot.

181 THE CASE FOR THE IMPERIAL CROWN
Prague, after 1350.
23 cm; 9¹/₈ in. high. Leather with rich, partly coloured carving, on the lid the Imperial Eagle and the Bohemian lion. Iron mountings. (XIII 30)

182 THE CASE FOR THE PROCESSIONAL CROSS WITH THE PARTICLE OF THE CROSS
Nürnberg, 1517.
34 cm; 13³/₈ in. high. Leather, lined with red parchment; brass mountings. (XIII 35)

183 CASE FOR THE TABLE-CLOTH RELIQUARY
Nürnberg, 1518.
61 cm; 24¹/₈ in. high. Leather, lined inside with red parchment, brass mountings. (XIII 37)
On the front the "Schwabenfeld" (Coat of Arms of Nürnberg).

184 CASE FOR THE APRON RELIQUARY
Nürnberg, 1518.
61·5 cm; 24¹/₄ in. high. Leather, lined inside with red parchment; brass mountings. (XIII 38)
On the front the "Schwabenfeld".

185 CASE FOR THE SMALLER RELICS
Nürnberg (?), end of 15th to beginning of 16th century (?).
57 × 17·5 cm; 22¹/₂ × 6⁷/₈ in. high. Leather, lined inside with red parchment; iron mountings. (XIII 40)

186 CASE FOR THE IMPERIAL CROSS
Nürnberg, 1495.
103 × 53·5 cm; 40¹/₄ × 21¹/₈ in. 29 cm; 11³/₈ in. high. Leather, lined with red parchment. Iron mountings. (XIII 41)
On the lid the "Jungfernadler" and the "Schwabenfeld" (both coats of arms of Nürnberg).

ECCLESIASTICAL TREASURE CHAMBER

I. MIDDLE AGES AND RENAISSANCE

1 MARSUPIUM (POUCH) OF KING STEPHEN OF HUNGARY
South Slav, 12th or 13th century.
18 cm; 7¹/₈ in. high. Silk, with silk and gold embroidery; Reverse side painted.
Pearls; gilded silver, garnets. (Kap. 186)
The cross with the garnets, the borders and the clasp is a German addition of
the 17th century. — According to tradition a little bag for relics, belonging
to King Stephen of Hungary.

2 MONILE (PENDANT) OF EMPEROR CHARLEMAGNE
German, 14th century.
14·5 cm; 5³/₄ in. high. Gold; semi-precious stones; rock crystal; onyx cameo;
wooden core. (D 128)
On the side the inscription: monile magni Karoli imperatoris veraciter de ligno
s(an)c(t)e crucis continens. Probably a Carolingian reliquary that a goldsmith
"restored" in such a way as to preserve the general form, the ornamentation
of precious stones and the gold plaques, while altering the details to suit con-
temporary taste. — The label on the back regarding its origin reads: "Dise
Particul vom Heyl. Creuz hat ... tus auf alln raisn vnd Schlachten bey sich
getrag(en); Vnd ist dieses Zu Prag von dem Churfürstn Zu Brandenburg
Kayser Ferd(inando) 3ᵗⁱᵒ 1651 verehrt worden." ("This particle of the Holy
Cross has ... carried on himself on all journeys and battles; and it was presented in Prague by the Elector of Brandenburg to Emperor Ferdinand III, in
1651.") The onyx cameo, portraying a maenad, is a Roman work of the 1st to
2nd century A. D. after a Greek model.

3 RELIQUARY WITH A RELIC OF ST. HEDWIG
German, 14th century.
8 cm; 3¹/₈ in. high. Gilded silver, glass. (Kap. 105)
Width 6 cm; 2³/₈ in. Relief in mother-of-pearl. (D 209)

4 ADORATION OF THE KINGS
German (Rhenish?), around 1500.

5 MONSTRANCE WITH RELICS
Venetian, 14th century. — German, 16th century.
68·5 cm; 27 in. high. Gilded silver; rock crystall; chrysoprase, amethysts, sapphires, garnets, corals, one ruby, pearls, one turquoise, mock jewels, parchment
miniatures. (Kap. 56)
The crucifix group engraved on the foot German, 3rd quarter of the 15th
century; the relic holder German, 16th century.

6 RELIC CASE
German, 14th century.
16 cm; 6¹/₄ in. high. Silver; the medallion with the Annunciation gilded silver
with niello work. Rock-crystal; velvet. (Kap. 187)
The faceted cylinder of rock-crystal probably Burgundian, 14th century.

6 a SILKEN CLOTH,

so-called hood of King Stephen of Hungary.

Byzantine (?), 11th century.

Red silk with embroidery in gold and coloured silk. (Kap. 187)

The cloth, formerly stitched together in the form of a simple hood, by tradition coming from King Stephen of Hungary, was previously folded and lying in the relic case, cat. No. 6.

7 SMALL CASE FOR RELICS

Siculo-Arabic, 12th century.

16·5 cm; 6¹/₂ in. high. Ivory, laid over wood; brass mountings; silver foil. (Kap. 55)

The silver band with the names of the Saints, relics of whom are preserved in the casket, is an addition of the 18th century. The feet and palmetto-shaped mountings on the lid are gothic additions.

8 CHALICE

Italian, end of the 14th century.

20·3 cm; 8 in. high. Gilded copper; the cup of gilded silver; enamel. (B 3)

An heirloom of Emperor Maximilian of Mexico.

9 CHALICE

South German, probably 1438.

19 cm; 7¹/₂ in. high. Silver, partly gilded. Viennese silver remark 1806/07, double-eagle. (B 1)

On the stem the inscription "got bues zv dier amen". On the base "AEIOV", the mark of the possessions of Emperor Frederick III, and the number of the year 1438. From this year there also exists a sundial with this mark (Collections of Sculpture and Handicrafts, 166). These two are the oldest objects with this collection of vowels that was later used as a device which has subsequently been explained in various ways. Given by the Academy of Wiener-Neustadt to the Castle Chapel in 1832.

10 THE HOLY FAMILY WITH ANGELS

Hans Daucher (born about 1485 in Augsburg, died 1537 in Stuttgart), 1518.

41·5 × 30·5 cm; 16³/₈ × 12 in. Relief on Solnhof stone with lead coloured tinting. Monogrammed H D and dated 1518; obliquely through the relief an old crack. (D 216)

The composition of the group of figures is based on drawings; the two angels are taken from Dürer's woodcut of the Holy Trinity, Mary with the Child is borrowed from a print of Marc Antonio Raimondi. The decoration of the foot of the column with crouching satyrs goes back to the epitaph of Jacob Fugger in the Fugger chapel of St. Anne's at Augsburg and is thus based on Dürer's ideas, as is proved by the drawings of the epitaph for Georg Fugger in the copper-engravings cabinet in Berlin. He in turn probably received the inspiration to this work in Italy (works of Riccio).

11 ROSARY DECADE

Flemish, 1st quarter of the 16th century.

Ivory; agate; gilded silver. (D 5)

The pendant represents a Memento Mori.

12   SAINT CHRISTOPHER

German, 2nd half of the 15th century.

Copper relief, gilded; in corresponding frame; mother-of-pearl, mock jewels. (D 170)

13   CHALICE

South-east German, around 1500.

23·2 cm; 9¹/₈ in. high. Silver, gilded except in a few places. Viennese silver remark 1806/07, remark 1809/10. (B 10)

13 a   CROSS WITH RELICS, BELONGING TO KING LOUIS THE GREAT OF HUNGARY

Hungarian (?), between 1370 and 1381; the stand Tuscan, first quarter of the 15th century.

The cross is 33·7 cm; 13³/₈ in., the foot 33·5 cm; 13¹/₄ in. high.

Gold, with slight traces of old enamel; gilded silver with traces of enamel; rubies, sapphires, emeralds, pearls, glass. (D 251/252)

With the coats of arms of Anjou, Old and New Hungary, and Poland. On the back the imperial double eagle (addition of the 16th century, together with the Bull of St. Luke).

Old property of the Treasure Chamber, purloined by a dishonest restorer, together with some other valuables, before 1879, when he replaced the originals with forgeries. Bought back from an art-dealer in 1957.

14   CHASUBLE WITH CHRIST ON THE TREE-CROSS

Bohemian or Austrian, around 1500.

Relief embroidery; red velvet. (A 11)

The velvet of the chasuble is of more recent date. — From the possessions of Emperor Maximilian of Mexico.

15   "WELSER" CHASUBLE

Upper-Italian, around 1500.

Silk embroidery; black silk rep; gold orphrey. Collections of Sculpture and Handicrafts. (5417)

From the possessions of the Welser family, whose coat of arms is to be found on the front. The embroidery was newly appliquéd in the 18th century and in the process a little piece of the embroidery was cut off.

16   FEMALE HEAD

South-German, around 1300.

37 cm; 14⁵/₈ in. high. Wood with damaged, old setting. Collections of Sculpture and Handicrafts. (9089)

Fragment of a wooden female sculpture (Madonna). From the Gustav Benda Foundation.

17   ST. CATHARINE, BUST WITH RELICS

Ulm, 2nd half of the 15th century.

43 cm; 17 in. high. Wood with damaged, coloured setting. Collections of Sculpture and Handicrafts. (9938)

The right-angled cavity in the stand was intended to contain the lost relic.

18 THE MOURNING FOR CHRIST
Netherlands (Brussels?), around 1510.
270 × 217 cm; 106 × 85¹/₂ in. Tapestry. Gobelins collection. (CXVIII)
Perhaps after a design of Quinten Metsys. — Acquired in 1930 from the nunnery of Nonnberg in Salzburg.

II. CORRIDOR OF VESTMENTS

19 "LADIES" VESTMENT
Vienna, middle of the 18th century. The brocade French, middle of the 18th century.
Red silk damask, gold brocade, silver orphreys. The gloves knitted, with silver embroidery. (A 29)
Donated by Empress Maria Theresia for the solemn feasts of the Order of the Star-Cross, the highest Order of noble ladies (whence the name of the vestment).

20 LUMEN FIDEI
Vienna, 1748.
Silver. Viennese town-mark of 1748, maker's mark P S, Viennese silver remark 1806/07, remark 1809/10. (C 50)

21 "FLECKERL" VESTMENT
Vienna, middle of the 18th century.
White silk appliquéd with different small pieces of brocade. Hence the name "Patchwork" vestment.

22 "ECKARTSAU" VESTMENT
Vienna, mid 18th century. The gold brocade French, mid 18th century.
Scarlet silk, inwoven with silver; gold brocade, orphreys of gold passementerie. (A 21)
Eckartsau is a castle in Lower Austria.

24 MONSTRANCE
Ath (Belgium), 1680.
84·5 cm; 33¹/₄ in. high. Silver. Town's mark of Ath, unexplained maker's mark, date letter. (B 9)

25 THE "BLUE AND SILVER" VESTMENT
Vienna (?), 3rd quarter of the 18th century.
Two silver brocades with blue background, partly embroidered. Silver orphreys. (A 36)

26 "PRAYER" VESTMENT
Vienna (?), between 1712 and 1740.
Silver- and gold brocade; coloured silk; silver. (A 34)
From the possessions of Emperor Charles VI.

27 CHALICE
Ludwig Schneider (died 1729 in Augsburg).
28·2 cm; 11¹/₈ in. high. Gilded silver; painted enamel; red and blue mock jewels.
Augsburg town-mark; maker's mark R₃ 727; on the cup the maker's mark J R.
Viennese remark 1806/07, remark 1809/10. (B 21)
Also the PATEN. Width 17·2 cm; 6³/₄ in. Gilded silver. Viennese silver hall-
mark 1806/07. (B 21)
On the cup and paten the coat of arms of Emperor Charles VI.

28 TWO CRUETS AND SALVER
Johann David Saller (died 1724 at Augsburg).
Salver 27·2 × 21·9 cm; 10³/₄ × 8⁵/₈ in., cruets 12 cm; 4³/₄ in. high. Silver, partly
gilded. Augsburg town-mark, maker's mark R₃ 760, Viennese silver remark
1806/07, remark 1809/10, double-eagle. (H 2)

29 RED CHASUBLE
*Vienna, mid 18th century. The gold brocade Persian, last third of the 17th
century.*
Scarlet silk damask; Persian gold brocade. Silver orphreys. (A 29)
Belongs to the "ladies' vestment" (No. 19).

30 GREEN PONTIFICAL VESTMENT
*Vienna (?), 3rd quarter of the 18th century. The brocade parts Persian, 2nd
half of the 17th century or early 18th century.*
Green, gold brocaded silk; Persian gold brocade, partly with silk and silver
embroidery. (A 33)

31 "GREEN PERSIAN" VESTMENT
*Vienna (?), mid 18th century. The brocade Persian, last third of the 17th
century.*
Green satin, Persian gold brocade, gold orphreys. (A 31)

32 RED CHASUBLE
*Vienna, 3rd quarter of the 18th century (?). The silver brocade Persian, last
third of the 17th century.*
Scarlet silk, gold brocaded; Persian silver brocade; silver orphreys. (A 108)

33 SIX CANDLESTICKS
Prague, Imperial Court workshop, beginning of the 17th century.
55·5 cm; 21⁷/₈ in. high. Jasper; gilded silver. (Kap. 89, 94)

34 "PAPAL" VESTMENT
Rome, about 1740—1758.
Silver lamé with rich gold and silk embroidery. (A 2)
On a chasuble a representation in needle painting of the baptism of Christ;
pearl trimming. In several places the coat of arms of Pope Benedict XIV
(1740—1758). The vestment is a gift of Pope Pius VI to Emperor Joseph II
on the occasion of his stay in Vienna in 1782.

III. COUNTER REFORMATION

35 PENDANT WITH PARCHMENT MINIATURES OF THE CRUCIFIXION AND THE BRAZEN SERPENT

Netherlands, end of the 16th century.

7·5 × 6·3 cm; $2^7/_8$ × $2^1/_2$ in. Rock-crystal; silver, gilded and partly enamelled. Import stamp for foreign gold and silver works (R₃ 7889). (D 32)

Elaborate version of a medallion used to ward off the plague.

36 ROSARY DECADE

German (Rhenish?), around 1600.

Rock-crystal; silver, gilded and painted; enamel. (D 184)

Between each two hemispheres of rock-crystal, which form a pearl, lie thin silver plaques with scenes from the bible and figures of saints.

37 PRAYER-BOOK OF EMPEROR FERDINAND II

South German, 1590.

Gold enamel cover, with the monograms of Christ and Mary, on the insides two parchment miniatures, representing Emperor Charlemagne and Mary; on the last one the date 1590; the pages of parchment with gold engraving. 4·8 × 6 cm; $1^7/_8$ × $2^3/_4$ in. Size of the pages 4·4 × 5·6 cm; $1^3/_4$ × $2^1/_8$ in. Viennese remark for gold 1806/07. (D 27)

The first pages of the book bear devices and signatures of members of the Habsburg and Wittelsbach families from the years 1590—1621. It is apparent, from the text of the prayers and these additions, that the book comes from the possessions of Ferdinand II, who received it from his parents Charles and Mary of Inner Austria when he went to the University of Ingolstadt in 1590. The first pages of the prayer-book were used as an album.

38 SCOURGE OF EMPRESS ANNE (THE WIFE OF EMPEROR MATTHIAS)

German before 1618.

Silver, partly gilded; silk; brass. (Kap. 147)

39 SCOURGE OF EMPRESS ELEONORA (the second wife of Emperor Ferdinand II)

German, 1st half of the 17th century.

Silver, partly gilded; silk, brass. (Kap. 148)

40 PILGRIM'S STAFF

Italian, about 1600 — German, 1606.

137·5 cm; 54 in. long. Bamboo pole with an open-work pommel. Silver, gilded; bamboo. (D 208)

With scenes from the Old and New Testaments, the lives of Saints Albertus, Cyrillus, Andreas Faesulanus and Angelus, and pictures of the twelve apostles. The legends are written partly in Latin and partly in Italian. On the pommel the Bavarian coat of arms with the inscription W(ILHELM) H(ERZOG) I(N) B(AYERN), the date 1606 and a coat of arms so far unidentified. The thorn is an addition of the 19th century. — The mountings and the pommel of gilded silver are German work. — From the possessions of Duke William V of Bavaria (reigned 1580—1597, died 1626).

41   CRUCIFIX
     Italian, 2nd half of the 16th century.
     54·5 cm; 21¹/₂ in. high. Rock crystal; gold enamel; gilded silver. (E 43)
     At the foot the adoration of the shepherds and the carrying of the cross.

42   TWO CANDLESTICKS
     Italian, 2nd half of the 16th century.
     20·8 cm; 8¹/₄ in. high. Rock crystal. Collections of Sculpture and Handicrafts.
     (2393, 2396)

43   GOLDEN ROSE TREE
     Rome (?), 1609.
     59·5 cm; 23¹/₂ in. high. Gold, enchased; silver; various semi-precious stones;
     rock crystal; glass; pearls. (Kap. 183)
     The vase bears the coat of arms of Pope Paul V Borghese (1605—1621) and
     the inscription PAVLVS V. PON(TIFEX) MAX(IMVS) ANN(O) IIII. The dragon's
     feet may recall the armorial animal of the Borghese, the dragon. According to
     tradition a present from the Pope to Archduchess (after 1612 Empress) Anne.
     (Cf. p. 25, No. 113)

44   SMALL FAMILY-ALTAR
     South German, last quarter of the 16th century.
     With relics of Saints Laurence, Nicholas, Christine, Deocharius, Habundus,
     Johanna, Dorothea, the companions of Saints Victor and Gereon and the
     11.000 virgins. 51·8 cm; 20³/₈ in. high. Ebony; gold enamel mountings; rubies;
     emeralds; pearls; cameos. (D 68)
     From the possessions of Duke William V of Bavaria, whose coat of arms
     adorns the pediment.

45   THE CRUCIFIXION OF CHRIST
     Hans Bol (born 1534 at Mecheln, died 1593 at Amsterdam), 1591.
     Width 6·8 cm; 2³/₄ in. Parchment miniature, signed H B O L 1591; in a standing
     frame of ebony with silver mountings. (German, end of the 16th century.)
     (D 96)

46   MITRE
     German (?), 2nd half of the 16th century.
     36 cm; 14¹/₄ in. high. Silk; silver paillettes; pearls; gilded silver. (Kap. 27)

47   THE RESURRECTION OF CHRIST
     Hans Bol (1534—1593), 1591.
     Width 7 cm; 2³/₄ in. Parchment miniature, signed H B O L 1591. In a standing
     frame of ebony with silver mountings. German, end of the 16th century.
     (D 97)

48   THE REVELATION TO THE SHEPHERDS
     Munich, beginning of the 17th century.
     37·5 cm; 14³/₄ in. high. Gilded silver; ebony; gold enamel; pearls; rubies; table-
     cut precious stones; rock crystal. (D 174)
     After a design of Hans Krumper.

49 OSTENSORY WITH VARIOUS RELICS OF CHRIST
South German, beginning of the 17th century.
48·5 cm; 19¹/₈ in. high. Ebony; gold enamel; rock crystal; diamonds; rubies (?); pearls. (D 23)
The garlands with painted enamel and the club-shaped pearls are additions of the 3rd quarter of the 17th century.

50 RELIQUARY WITH A WAX BUST OF ST. VALERIAN AND A RELIC OF ST. MAURICE
Munich, beginning of the 17th century.
36 cm; 14¹/₄ in. high. Wax; cloth; ebony; gold enamel; gilded bronze. (D 70)
After a design of Hans Krumper.

51 OSTENSORY WITH PIETÀ
South German, around 1600.
21 cm; 8¹/₄ in. high. Ebony; silver, partly gilded; wax, painted with colours; pearls. (D 195)

52 SMALL PRIVATE ALTAR OF EMPRESS ANNE
South German, beginning of the 17th century.
67·5 cm; 26⁵/₈ in. high. Ebony; the flat pictures of pieces of cloth and hair, the faces and hands of painted parchment; the plastic representations of coloured wax, decorated with tinsel and coloured paper. (Kap. 333)
An object of religious life in everyday use, it is clearly differentiated from the artisticaly adorned small altars which perhaps already served more representative purposes. The multiplicity of the portraits offers the worshipper manifold inspiration, as on the other hand the relics locked in drawers are reserved solely for the faithful veneration and personal use of the possessor. — Its attribution to Empress Anne is traditional, but cannot be more closely established.

53 OSTENSORY WITH A PORTRAIT OF CHRIST ON THE MOUNT OF OLIVES
South German, around 1600.
21·5 cm; 8¹/₂ in. high. Ebony; silver, partly gilded and partly enamelled; pearls; wax, painted with colours. (D 196)

54 RELIQUARY WITH A WAX BUST OF ST. TIBURTIUS AND A RELIC OF ST. CRISPINUS
Munich, beginning of the 17th century.
36 cm; 14¹/₄ in. high. Wax; cloth; ebony; gold enamel; gilded bronze. (D 71)
After a design of Hans Krumper.

55 SMALL FAMILY-ALTAR
Ottavio Miseroni (known to be at the Imperial Court at Prague after 1588, died at Prague in 1624).
With marquetry ("commesso"), portraying Mary with the Child (marked OTT. M.) and a fragment "Von unnser liewen Frauen Hemet" ("of our dear Lady's robe"). On the pediment a cameo with the head of Mary.
30·5 cm; 12 in. high. Jasper; agate; lapis lazuli; diamonds; rubies; pearls; gold enamel; gilded silver. (Kap. 219)

56 SMALL FAMILY-ALTAR WITH A BONE OF ST. TIMOTHY
Prague, Imperial Court workshop, 1st quarter of the 17th century.
44 cm; 17³/₈ in. high. Ebony; jasper; gold enamel; painter's enamel; diamonds;
rubies; pearls; cloth. (Kap. 222)
On the pediments relics of Christ.
The centre-plate from Vienna, middle of the 17th century.

57 CROSS WITH RELICS
German, around 1600.
43 cm; 17 in. high. Ebony; gilded, partly cold enamelled silver; parchment miniatures under glass. (E 3)

58 SMALL FAMILY-ALTAR WITH A CRUCIFIXION GROUP
South German, 1st quarter of the 17th century.
44·2 cm; 17¹/₂ in. high. Ebony; jasper; jasper agate; agate; gold enamel; diamonds; rubies; pearls. (Kap. 221)
In the pediment a thorn from Christ's crown.

59 SMALL FAMILY-ALTAR
*Ottavio Miseroni (known to be at the Imperial Court in Prague after 1588,
died in 1624 at Prague).*
With marquetry ("commesso") portraying St. Anne with Mary and Christ
(marked OTT. MIS.) and a relic of St. Anne. In the pediment a cameo with a
head of Christ. 33 cm; 13 in. high. Jasper; agate; lapis lazuli; diamonds; rubies;
pearls; gold enamel; gilded silver. (Kap. 220)

60 OSTENSORY WITH A THORN OF CHRIST'S CROWN
South German, end of the 16th century.
32 cm; 12⁵/₈ in. high. Gold enamel; silver; rock-crystal. Viennese silver remark
1806/07, remark 1809/10, double eagle. (D 67)
Various relics in one drawer.

61 CASKET WITH A RELIC OF SAINT FELIX
Italian, 16th century.
4·2 cm; 1⁵/₈ in. high. Rock-crystal in gold enamel work. (D 92)
The figurate parts of the rock-crystal plaques repeat the three altar-step pictures of Raffaelo Santi for the sculpture (Vatican, Pinacotheca).

62 OSTENSORY WITH A RELIC OF ST. STANISLAUS, BISHOP OF CRACOW
Augsburg (Matthäus Wallbaum?), 1597.
28 cm; 11 in. high. Gold enamel; one ruby; smoky topaz; Viennese remark for
gold 1806/07. (D 112)
Above the nodus the Polish eagle, showing as breast plate the coat of arms
of the Radziwil. On the back the Swedish escutcheon. On the foot the dedi-
cation: GEOR(GIV)S CARD(INA)LIS RADZIWIL EP(ISCOP)VS CRACOVIEN(SIS) ET
EIVSDEM ECCL(ESI)AE CAP(ITV)LVM SER(ENISSI)MAE MARIAE ARCHIDVCISSAE
AVSTRIAE DE BRACHIO S(ANCTI) STANISLAI EP(ISCOP)I ET MARTYRIS D(E)-
D(ERVNT) MDXCVII.

63 OSTENSORY WITH A THORN OF CHRIST'S CROWN AND RELICS OF SAINTS FABIAN, SEBASTIAN AND MAXIMILIAN
South German (Augsburg?), 1592.
50·4 cm; 19⁷/₈ in. high. Ebony; gold enamel; rock-crystal; diamonds; rubies; emeralds; pearls. (D 21)
On the relic-holder in the stand the date 1592. Crowned with an allegory of faith.

64 OSTENSORY WITH A PIECE OF THE REED-MACE OF CHRIST AND RELICS OF SAINTS PETER, SIGMUND AND LAMBERT
South German, 1st half of the 17th century (a few of the parts Augsburg?, around 1592).
54·8 cm; 21⁵/₈ in. high. Ebony; gold; gold enamel; painted enamel; glass; rubies; diamonds; emeralds; pearls. (D 22)
Crowned with a figure of St. Peter.

65 VASE FOR RELICS
South German, beginning of the 17th century.
46 cm; 18¹/₈ in. high. Rock-crystal; gold enamel; ebony; diamonds; pearls. (Kap. 46)
The cutting Italian (probably from Milan). The topmost pyramid and the relics are missing.

66 VASE FOR RELICS
South German, beginning of the 17th century. — Vienna (?), about 1800.
26·5 cm; 10³/₈ in. high. Rock-crystal; gold enamel; gold; silver; ebony. (Kap. 85)

67 VASE FOR RELICS
South German, beginning of the 17th century. — Vienna (?), about 1800.
24 cm; 9¹/₂ in. high. Rock-crystal; gold enamel; gold; silver; ebony. (Kap. 86)

68 SMALL FAMILY-ALTAR
Matthäus Wallbaum (born 1554 in Kiel, died 1632 in Augsburg), 1588.
36·6 cm; 14³/₈ in. high. Ebony; partly gilded silver. (D 172)
The silver relief with the Madonna and Child on a throne is a reduced imitation of the main relief of the Altar of Wallbaum in Castle Frederiksborg (Denmark). From the possessions of Emperor Matthias.

69 SMALL FAMILY-ALTAR (TRIPTYCHON)
Matthäus Wallbaum (1554—1632), 1588.
40·5 cm; 16 in. high. Ebony; partly gilded silver; miniatures on copper. Augsburg town-mark R₃ 126, maker's mark R₃ 428. The miniature with the adoration of shepherds marked with "L W 1588". (D 178)
From the possessions of Emperor Matthias.

70 OSTENSORY WITH RELICS OF SEVERAL SAINTS
Matthäus Wallbaum (1554—1632), 1588 (?).
49·8 cm; 19³/₄ in. high. Ebony; partly gilded silver. Augsburg town-mark R₃ 126, maker's mark R₃ 428. (D 89)
The inscription concerning the relics names the following saints: Matthew, Lucius, Candidus, Eustorgius, Mary Magdalene, Cecilianus, Valentinianus, Zoimus, Amanda, Laurence, John, Merita, Thecla, Verena, Udalrich and Albert.

71 SMALL FAMILY-ALTAR (TRIPTYCHON)
    Matthäus Wallbaum (1554—1632), 1588.
    40·7 cm; 16 in. high. Ebony; partly gilded silver; miniatures on copper. (D 179)
    Cf. No. 69.

72 SMALL FAMILY-ALTAR
    Matthäus Wallbaum (1554—1632).
    36·4 cm; 14³/₈ in. high. Ebony; partly gilded silver. (D 173)
    Cf. No. 68.

73 OSTENSORY WITH RELICS OF ST. MARY MAGDALENE AND TWO
    UNNAMED SAINTS
    Augsburg, about 1600 (Workshop of Matthäus Wallbaum).
    46·8 cm; 18¹/₂ in. high. Ebony; silver, partly gilded. (D 91)

74 OSTENSORY WITH RELICS OF SAINTS SEBASTIAN AND APOLLINARIS,
    AND OF AN UNKNOWN SAINT
    Augsburg, about 1600 (Workshop of Matthäus Wallbaum).
    46·8 cm; 18¹/₂ in. high. Ebony; silver, partly gilded. (D 90)

75 SMALL ALTAR WITH SIDES
    South German, 1st half of the 17th century.
    26 cm; 10¹/₄ in. high. Ebony; silver, cast, partly with remains of a former gil-
    ding. (D 182)
    The altar is a pastiche, mainly composed of parts of a small family-altar of
    Matthäus Wallbaum. The other reliefs are probably South German works of
    the same period.

76 SAINT ANNE WITH MARY AND CHRIST AND WITH ST. JOHN
    AS A CHILD
    North Italian beginning of the 17th century.
    34·1 cm; 13¹/₂ in. high. Silver relief in an ebony frame with bronze mountings.
    (D 177)
    After the painting "Madonna del divino amore" at Naples (attributed to
    Raphael, Giulio Romano, or Francesco Penni).

77 SMALL ALTAR
    (South?) German, 1st quarter of the 17th century.
    With a parchment miniature of the Madonna with the child Jesus.
    46·2 cm; 18¹/₄ in. high. Ebony; silver, partly gilded; blue enamel. (D 175)
    Base and frame were created by different masters and actually do not belong
    together.

78 CRUCIFIX
    South German, end of the 16th century.
    80·3 cm; 32 in. high. With partly gilded silver inlay. (E 49)

79 SMALL ALTAR
    South German, 1st quarter of the 17th century.
    With a parchment miniature of the Annunciation, and with relics of Saints
    Stephen, Lucy, Luke, Bartholomew, Laurence, Matthew, Blasius and Gregorius.

48·5 cm; 19¹/₄ in. high. Ebony; silver, partly gilded; bronce, gilded; parchment miniature. (D 17)

80 SMALL ALTAR

South German, 1st quarter of the 17th century.

With Saints Augustine, Peter, John the Baptist, Hieronymus, and an unidentifiable saint in the cope, a figure of the devil at his feet; crowned with a Madonna and Child. 37·2 cm; 14³/₄ in. high. Ebony; silver (some mountings gilded, one enamelled); two emeralds. (D 183)

81 THE REST ON THE FLIGHT TO EGYPT

North Italian, beginning of the 17th century.

31·1 cm; 12¹/₄ in. high. Silver relief, in an ebony frame with gilded bronze mountings. (D 176)

After a painting by Federico Barrocci at Rome, Vatikan, Pinacotheca. E. Tietze-Conrat assumes that the link between the two was provided by an engraving by Cornelis Cort.

82 CRUCIFIXION

Andreas Hamburger (Augsburg, died 1657), around 1620.

40 × 60 cm; 15³/₄ × 23³/₄ in. Silver reliefs, partly gilded, cut out and appliquéd on reddish-brown velvet; in a gilded wooden frame. Remark 1809/10. (Kap. 40)

83 THE BODY OF CHRIST, CARRIED BY TWO ANGELS

North Italian, 1st half of the 17th century.

31·5 × 38·4 cm; 12³/₈ × 15¹/₈ in. Relief in gilded bronze. (D 218)

84 CRUCIFIXION GROUP

Giambologna-Workshop. — South German, 1st quarter of the 17th century.

Cross 101·5 cm; 40 in., Mary 38·6 cm; 15¹/₄ in., John 39·6 cm; 15⁵/₈ in., Mary Magdalena 32 cm; 12⁵/₈ in. high. Bronze; mounted on a wooden stand. (E 34) The group is inspired by Giambologna if it is not indeed based on a lost model by him. Executed by a south German master from the workshop of Hubert Gerhard. The crucified figure is much more closely related to the works of Giambologna. Its craftsman has to be sought in the workshop of Giambologna himself. The wooden stand probably 18th century.

85 CASKET FOR RELICS

Venetian (?), end of 16th century.

25 cm; 9³/₄ in. high. Ebony, partly painted with gold; covered with sardonyx and lapis lazuli plates, inside a parchment miniature with the Assumption of Mary; red silk. (D 185)

The miniature probably by Georg Hoefnagel.

IV. BAROQUE

86 CHRIST AS MAN OF SORROWS IN A SMALL TEMPLE

South German, mid 17th century. — The Christ probably Spanish, 1st half of the 17 century.

Ivory, ebony; silver, partly gilded. Almandines. (Kap. 297)

Crowned by a relic case with a piece of the pillar where Christ was scourged; in the drawers of the stand different relics. — The scourging pillar on which Christ was leaning is lost.

87   MADONNA WITH CHILD AND THE CHILD JOHN

Adam Lenckhardt (born 1610 in Würzburg, died 1661 in Vienna).
18 cm; 7$^1/_8$ in. high. Ivory. Marked A L. On an ebony stand. (D 211)

88   THE RISEN CHRIST

South(?)-German, 1st half of the 17th century.
29 cm; 11$^3/_8$ in. high. Ivory. On an ebony stand of the same period. (D 210)
Reversed, varied repetition of the statue by Michelangelo in Rome, Santa Maria sopra Minerva.

89   PATRON OF BAVARIA

Augsburg, after 1613.
Statuette with a piece of the veil of Mary in the stand. 42·5 cm; 16$^3/_4$ in. high. Silver, partly gilded. Augsburg town-mark, maker's mark R$_3$ 3851, remark 1809/10, double eagle. (Kap. 21) Reversed variation of Hubert Gerhard's Patrona Bavariae, Munich (finished 1613). The maker's mark was wrongly attributed by Rosenberg to Jeremias Wild, who died in 1608.

90   THE ADORATION OF THE KINGS

South German (Augsburg?), about 1600.
11·2 cm × 16 cm; 4$^3/_8$ × 6$^1/_4$ in. Silver relief. Remark 1809/10. (Kap. 2)

91   MARY WITH THE CHILD AND ANGELS

Augsburg, 1st half of the 17th century.
Silver, chased, partly gilded, and cut out; mounted on a plaque covered with red velvet (30 × 49 cm; 11$^3/_4$ × 19$^3/_8$ in.). (Kap. 208)

92   STATUETTE OF ST. LEOPOLD

Augsburg, 1st quarter of the 17th century.
With a relic of the saint. 8·9 cm; 3$^1/_2$ in. high. Silver, partly gilded; rock crystal. Viennese remark 1806/07. (D 122)
Probably part of a larger work that has been lost.

93   PRAYER BOOK OF EMPRESS CLAUDIA FELICITAS

Printed 1674 in Konstanz. The cover South German (Augsburg?), about 1674.
7·7 × 12·5 cm; 3$^1/_4$ × 4$^7/_8$ in. Silver; paper. (Kap. 16)
The book is written by the Capucine Father Lucianus Montifontanus, is dedicated to the Empress and treats of the life and martyrdom of St. Fidelis of Sigmaringen.

94   ST. JOSEPH

Augsburg, 1st quarter of the 17th century.
Statuette with a piece of the saint's mantle in the stand. 41 cm; 16$^1/_8$ in. high. Silver, partly gilded. Augsburg town-mark, maker's mark R$_3$ 544, remark 1809/10, double-eagle. (Kap. 22)

95 THE CORONATION OF MARY
Augsburg, beginning of the 17th century.
18·3 × 24·7 cm; 7¹/₄ × 9⁵/₈ in. Silver relief. Augsburg town-mark, maker's mark
R₃ 484. (Kap. 194)
Probably after a design of Peter Candid.

96 RELIQUARY OF ST. EUSTACE
Augsburg, beginning of the 17th century.
41·5 cm; 16³/₈ in. high. Silver, partly gilded; onyx. Augsburg town-mark,
maker's mark R₃ 459, remark 1809/10. (Kap. 48)

97 ALLEGORY ON THE DEATH OF EMPEROR FERDINAND III
(died 11th March 1657)
Daniel Neuberger (born 1621 at Augsburg, died 1680 at Regensburg).
Wax; glittering, coloured sand. In a small ebony case 46·5 × 36·5 cm; 18³/₈ ×
14³/₈ in. (Kap. 244)

98 RELIQUARY OF ST. MARY
Augsburg, beginning of the 17th century.
34·5 cm; 13⁵/₈ in. high. Silver, partly gilded; mother-of-pearl relief; rock
crystal, Augsburg town-mark, maker's mark R₃ 459, remark 1809/10. (Kap. 50)

99 ADORATION OF THE SHEPHERDS
South German (Augsburg?), around 1600.
15·3 × 20 cm; 6 ×7⁷/₈ in. Silver relief. (Kap. 3)
After a lost painting of Hans von Aachen (engraving by Egidus Sadeler in
1588).

100 STOUP
South German, last quarter of the 17th century.
Portraying the adoration of the shepherds. 20·7 cm; 8¹/₄ in. high. Silver, gilded;
painted enamel; gold enamel; rock crystal, emeralds, rubies, diamonds, various
semi-precious stones. Viennese remark 1806/07. (D 188)
The adoration of the shepherds, after a painting of Joseph Heintz.

101 OSTENSORY WITH A NAIL OF CHRIST'S CROSS
Vienna (?), 3rd quarter of the 17th century.
79·6 cm; 31¹/₂ in. high. Gold partly with painted enamel; gilded silver; topazes, emeralds, sapphires, amethysts, aquamarine, hyacinth, turquoises,
garnets; mock jewels. (D 62)

102 RELIQUARY WITH RELICS OF THE THREE MAGI
Augsburg, mid 17th century.
30 cm; 11³/₄ in. high. Silver, gilded; on the figure of Caspar cold enamel; lapis
lazuli. Augsburg town-mark, two unidentified maker's marks. (D 38)
The figure of Caspar: around 1830—1840.

103 SMALL FAMILY-ALTAR
South German, 2nd—3rd quarter of the 17th century.
With a thorn of Christ's Crown and relics of Saints Stephen, Eustace, Andrew
and George. 70 cm; 27¹/₂ in. high. Ebony; gold enamel; enamelled, gilded

silver; gilded, partly enamelled bronce; chrysolites; almandines; pearls; rock crystal; garnets. (D 59)

From the possessions of Emperor Leopold I.

104 RELIQUARY WITH A PARTICLE OF THE HOLY CROSS
Vienna (?), 1668.
53·5 cm; 21 in. high. Silver, gilded; painted enamel on gold foil; garnets; chrysoprase, amethysts, agates, cornelians, brilliants, diamonds and rock crystal. Viennese remark of 1806/07, remark 1809/10. (D 25)
The crown of brilliants over the cross dates from the 18th century. The relic-cross was previously fastened to the centre of the niche, as is shown by the holes at the bottom of the niche which are set higher up and today unused.
This article is of special historical significance. When part of the Castle burnt down in February 1668, the particle — then in the possessions of the widowed Empress Eleonora — remained miraculously preserved and this gave occasion to the founding of the Star-cross Order.

105 SMALL FAMILY-ALTAR
South German, 2nd—3rd quarters of the 17th century. With five unknown relics.
70 cm; 27¹/₂ in. high. Ebony; gold enamel; enamelled, gilded silver; gilded, partly enamelled bronze; chrysolites; almandines; pearls; garnets; rock crystal. (D 63)
From the possessions of Emperor Leopold I.

106 PASTORALE
German, 2nd half of the 17th century.
185 cm; 73 in. high. "Ainkhürn" (narwhal horn); partly gilded silver; mock jewels. (Kap. 26)
Concerning "Ainkhürn", see page 21, No. 81.

107 THE SCOURGING OF CHRIST
Allessandro Algardi (born 1602 in Bologna, died 1654 in Rome).
Group in bronze, gilded, on an ebony plinth with a gilded bronze pillar, covered with lapis lazuli. Christ 21·6 cm; 8¹/₂ in., left tormentor 23·2 cm; 9¹/₈ in., right tormentor 21·8 cm; 8⁵/₈ in. high. (D 127)

108 GOLDEN CHASUBLE
Vienna (?), 18th century. The gold brocade Persian, last quarter of the 17th century.
Persian gold brocade; silver orphreys. (A 610)

109 RED CHASUBLE
Milan (?), 1st half of the 18th century.
Cherry red silk with gold and silver embroidery. (A 115)
The silk is supposed to have been taken from a robe of St. Charles Borromeo.

110 POPE LEO THE GREAT AND ATTILA, KING OF THE HUNS
Alessandro Algardi (born 1602 in Bologna, died 1654 in Rome).
98 cm; 38³/₄ in. high. Bronze, gilded. (D 164)

Cast after the Bozzetto (model) for the monumental relief in St. Peter's at Rome, that was created from 1646—1650 by Algardi with the help of Domenico Guidi. Following Pascoli's "Vita di Ercole Ferrata", Ferrata, a pupil of Algardi, probably carried out the casting.

V. BAROQUE AND ROCOCO

111 CRUCIFIX
German, mid 17th century.
Christ 44 cm; $17^3/_8$ in. high. Ivory; polished black wood. (E 1)

112 CHRIST BEARING THE CROSS
Johann Caspar Schenk (employed in 1665 as "Court ivory carver" in Vienna, died there 1674).
9×13.5 cm; $3^1/_2 \times 5^1/_4$ in. Ivory relief, monogrammed I C S. On an ebony plaque. (D 200)
Reserved after an etching of Jaques Callot.

113 CHRIST AND THE TWO ROBBERS ON THE CROSS
Leonhard Kern (born 1585 or 1588, died 1662 at Hall in Swabia).
Christ 36.3 cm; $14^3/_8$ in., the good robber 33 cm; 13 in., the wicked robber 35.5 cm; 14 in. high. Ivory, mahogany. (The two robbers E 4, Christ E 45)

114 MARTYRDOM OF SAINTS
Johann Caspar Schenk (employed in 1665 as "Court ivory-carver" in Vienna, died there 1674).
9×14 cm; $3^1/_2 \times 5^1/_2$ in. Ivory relief, monogrammed I C S. On an ebony plaque. (D 199)

115 THE SCOURGING OF CHRIST
German, mid 17th century.
35.5×46 cm; $14 \times 18^1/_4$ in. Ivory relief in an ebony frame. (Kap. 324)

116 THE MOURNING FOR CHRIST
Leonhard Kern (born 1585 or 1588, died 1662 at Hall in Swabia).
40.2×24.5 cm; $15^7/_8 \times 9^3/_4$ in. Ivory relief in a brown wooden casket from the same period, with glass. (D 198)

117 CHRIST'S CROWNING WITH THORNS
German, mid 17th century.
35.5×46 cm; $14 \times 18^1/_4$ in. Ivory relief in an ebony frame. (Kap. 324)

118 "MANTLE" VESTMENT
Vienna, 1736.
French gold rep (before 1736); silver lamé with appliqué of shaded ribbons and gimps; silver orphreys. (A 17)
From the mantle worn by Franz Stephan of Lorraine at his marriage to Maria Theresia (12th February, 1736).

119 TRIMMING FOR ALBS (LACE)
Brussels, 1st half of the 18th century.
Lace. (A 187)

120 TRIMMING FOR ALBS (LACE)
Brussels, 1st half of the 18th century.
Lace. (A 199)

121 MONSTRANCE
Vienna, 1760.
71^1/$_2$ cm; 28 in. high. Gilded silver, partly enamelled; diamonds; rubies; emeralds; sapphires; hyacinths.
Viennese town-mark 1760, unclear maker's mark.
Presumably by the Viennese goldsmith Muthreich.
From the Ursuline Convent, Vienna.

122 CRUCIFIXION GROUP (FRAGMENT)
Matthias Steinle (born around 1644, died 1727 in Vienna).
45·5 cm; 18 in. high. Ivory; ebony. Signed on the base plaque of Magdalene. Steinle. (E 45)

123 CRUCIFIX
Austrian, around 1710—1720.
87·5 cm; 34^1/$_2$ in. high. Ivory; polished black wood; almandine. (E 46)

124 PACIFICALE
Vienna, 1704.
29 cm; 11^1/$_2$ in. high. Gold; gold enamel; rock crystal; diamonds; amethysts; emeralds; rubies; sapphires; garnets; pearls; lapis lazuli; corals; cornelian and hyacinth cameos; mother-of-pearl; parchment miniatures. Signed on the back: "Von Gebrüder Palm 1704". (Kap. 45) The Palm brothers, a Viennese family of bankers, were probably the donators of the pacificale.
A pacificale is a reliquary with a particle of the Cross, that can be used at the kiss of peace in Solemn Mass.

125 PACIFICALE
Johann Baptist Känischbauer von Hohenried (born 1668 at Angern, Lower Austria, died 1739 at Vienna), 1726.
25·3 cm; 10 in. high. Gold, partly enamelled; diamonds; rubies; rock crystal; pearls; glass cut as brilliants; the settings of the mock jewels on the radiant wreath are of gilded silver. Behind the movable bull-symbol signed and dated: "Jo: Känischbaur / v. Hohen Ried / R. K. M. Kamer / Künstler 1726". Viennese remark 1806/07 for gold, remark for silver 1809/10. (D 39)
The reliquary represents a glorification of the Holy Cross. There is a strong supposition that a model for the Pacificale already existed. Similar works are to be found by Johann Bernhard Fischer von Erlach (high altar at Mariazell, executed by Känischbaur).

126 OSTENSORY WITH A RELIC OF ST. CHARLES BORROMEO
Milan (?), 1766.
27·5 cm; 10^7/$_8$ in. high. Cased gold; gilded silver; rock crystal; wooden core. Viennese gold remark 1806/07, remark for silver 1809/10. (D 46)

127 CHALICE
Vienna, 1747.
29·4 cm; 11⁵/₈ in. high. Gilded silver; painted enamel; emeralds; amethysts; rubies; almandines; diamonds. Viennese town-mark of 1747, Viennese silver remark 1806/07. (B 7)
On the inner side of the foot a silver plaque with the coat of arms of the Forgach family, and an inscription of 1748 naming Paul Count Forgach, Bishop of Großwardein, as possessor.

128 CHALICE
J. Hueber (active 2nd half of the 18th century in Vienna), 1767.
30 cm; 11⁷/₈ in. high. Gilded silver. Viennese town-mark of 1767, maker's mark R₃ 7956, Viennese silver remark 1806/07, remark 1809/10. (B 4)

129 CHALICE
Joseph Moser (active in the 2nd half of the 18th century in Vienna), 1775.
27·2 cm; 10³/₄ in. high. Gilded silver; painted enamel; diamonds; rubies; emeralds; amethysts; garnets. Viennese town-mark of 1775, maker's mark R₃ 7948, Viennese silver remark 1806/07, remark 1809/10. (B 8)

130 TORTOISE-SHELL CASKET
German (Dresden?), 1st quarter of the 18th century.
15·2 cm; 6 in. high. Crowned by an onyx cameo portraying St. Hieronymus; torsoise-shell; silver, gilded, partly with cold enamel; gold enamel; mother-of-pearl; bone; diamonds. (D 192)
In the sides are niches, the lower parts forming doors, with small figures which cannot be indentified with certainty. Behind these doors, scenes from the Passion of Christ could be seen. The Rising Christ is all that has been preserved. Two small female figures in gold enamel, Ecclesia and Synagoge, from the workshop of Matthäus Wallbaum (1554—1632).

131 ALTAR SET FOR JOURNEYS (H 3)
Florence (?), 1st half of the 18th century.
Consists of:
a) Chalice. 24 cm; 9¹/₂ in. high. Gilded silver. Circular engraving (four legged animal — lion or panther? — over F), R₃ 7327, R₃ 7488.
b) Two cruets. 18·8 cm; 7³/₈ in. high. Silver, glass. R₃ 7329.
c) Lumen fidei. 21·5 cm; 8¹/₂ in. long. Silver. Circular engraving as under a, R₃ 7327, R₃ 7488.
d) Candle-snuffers. 13·2 cm; 5¹/₄ in. long. Silver. Circular engraving as under a, R₃ 7329.
e) Aspergilum. Diameter 13·4 cm; 5¹/₄ in. Silver. Circular engraving as under a, R₃ 7327, R₃ 7329, R₃ 7488.
f) Holy water vessel. 22·7 cm; 8⁷/₈ in. long. Silver.
g) Silver relief portraying the Holy Trinity. 18 cm; 7¹/₈ in. high. Circular engraving as under a, R₃ 7327, R₃ 7488.
h) Missal, printed in Venice, 1823. Binding: velvet with gold impression; mountings of gilded silver. 17 × 25 cm; 6⁵/₈ × 9⁷/₈ in.
To such altar sets for court journeys also belongs the large Mass trunk, the lid of which is usually decorated on the inside with an altar picture; in the trunk were also packed, apart from the objects mentioned, small candlesticks that could be dismantled, a set of light Mass vestments, the linen for the altar, etc. The missal is an addition of 1823.

132   "PAPERL" VESTMENT (THE SO-CALLED PARROT'S VESTMENT)
      Vienna, about 1712—1740.

Silver and flat silk embroidery on a laid-on gold background; appliqué of silk materials; silver orphreys. (A 4)

The cloth with flowers and birds (whence the name of the vestment) from a wall-tapestry of a Spanish Castle (Madrid?) of the late 17th century was altered into a vestment at the command of Empress Elizabeth Christine. At that time the heads and claws of the birds were hidden by flowered appliqué.

133   ALB TRIMMING (LACE)
      Brussels, 1st half of the 18th century.
      Lace. (A 200)

134   ALB TRIMMING (LACE)
      Brussels, 1st half of the 18th century.
      Lace. (A 201)

135   MITRE
      Austrian, 1712—1740.

Yellow silk inwoven with gold and with gold and silver embroidery. (A 158)
The mitre bears the monogram and device of Emperor Charles VI.

136   OSTENSORY WITH MINIATURE PICTURES OF CHRIST AND MARY
      Austrian (?), last third of the 17th century.

39·5 cm; 15^1/$_2$ in. high. Rock crystal; silver, partly gilded. Viennese remark 1806/07. (D 219)

Both miniatures are probably from the Netherlands, dating from the beginning of the 17th century.

137   ST. FELIX OF CANTALICO

Joseph Moser (working in the second half of the 18th century in Vienna), 1758.
Bust with a relic of the saint. 28·8 cm; 11^1/$_4$ in. high. Silver. Viennese town-mark of 1758, maker's mark R$_3$ 7948, remark 1809/10. Double eagle. (Kap. 14)
Dedication of the children of Empress Maria Theresia, mentioned on the back of the base: Joseph, Maria Anna, Maria Christine, Caroline, Antonia and Charles.

138   MONSTRANCE
      Vienna, 1704.

66 cm; 26 in. high. Silver, partly gilded; amethyst; topazes; turquoises; garnets; rock crystals; pearls; mock jewelry; glass. Viennese town-mark 1704, maker's mark ZF, remark 1809/10, double eagle. (Kap. 88)

The idea of shaping the Custodia in the figure of Mary is based on Byzantine precedents (Platytera).

139   RELIQUARY WITH A PARTICLE OF THE CROSS
      Matthias Unverdorben (?) (Traceable after 1709 as a citizen of Salzburg).

32·7 cm; 12^7/$_8$ in. high. Silver partly gilded; rock-crystal; mock jewelry. Unclear town-mark, maker's mark M V. Salzburg remark for silver 1806/07. (D 220)
In the form of a cross, our Lady of Sorrows kneeling in front.
Taken over from the Salzburg private chapel in 1910. — On the base the coat of arms of the Prince-Archbishop of Salzburg, Franz Anton Count of Harrach (reigned 1709—1727).

140   OSTENSORY WITH A RELIC OF ST. ANNE

Joseph Moser (working in the 2nd half of the 18th century in Vienna), 1760.
28·3 cm; 11¹/₄ in. high. Silver, chased. Viennese town-mark 1760, maker's mark
R₃ 7948. Viennese silver remark 1806/07, remark for silver 1809/10. (D 24)

141   ST. DONATUS, BUST WITH RELICS

Joseph Moser (working in the 2nd half of the 18th century in Vienna), 1766.
34·3 cm; 13¹/₂ in. high. Silver; gilded bronze. Viennese silver remark 1806/07,
remark 1809/10. (D 20)

142   ST. PETER, BUST WITH RELICS

Vienna (Joseph Moser?), before 1758.
33 cm; 13 in. high. Silver, gilded bronze. Viennese silver remark 1806/07, remark 1809/10. (D 98)

143   SHRINE WITH RELICS OF THE HOLY INNOCENTS

Vienna (?), mid 18th century.
24 cm; 9¹/₂ in. high. Silver, gilded. Viennese silver remark 1806/07. (D 60)

144   ST. PAUL, BUST WITH RELICS

Vienna (Joseph Moser?), before 1758.
32·8 cm; 13 in. high. Silver; gilded bronze. Viennese remark 1806/07, remark
1809/10. (D 121)

145   ST. ANNE, BUST WITH RELICS

Joseph Moser (working 2nd half of the 18th century in Vienna), 1779.
33·7 cm; 13¹/₄ in. high. Silver; gilded bronze. Viennese town-mark of 1779,
maker's mark R₃ 7948, Viennese silver remark 1806/07, remark 1809/10.
(D 136)

146   BOUQUET OF SILVER FLOWERS IN A STONE VASE

German, last quarter of the 17th century. — 2nd third of the 18th century.
63·5 cm; 25 in. high. Silver; stone; bronze, gilded. H. H. engraved on a flower
stalk. (D 52)

147   SUDARIUM OF VERONICA

Italian, about 1617 — Austrian, about 1800.
58·5 × 48·4 cm; 23 × 19 in. In an ebony frame and a silver frame. Silver,
partly gilded; ebony; mother-of-pearl; gilded copper; onyx cameos; ivory.
Viennese remark 1806/07, remark 1809/10. (D 108)
The face impressed in the linen is framed by four gilded copper plates, on
which is engraved the excommunication by Pope Paul V of any person making
a copy of the Sudarium without Papal permission. The inscription dated 1617.
The appearance of the Sudarium at several places has been explained by the
folding of the cloth.

148   BOUQUET OF SILVER FLOWERS IN A STONE VASE

German, last quarter of the 17th century to 2nd third of the 18th century.
62 cm; 24³/₈ in. high. Silver; stone; bronze, gilded. H. H. engraved on a flower
stalk. (D 53)

149   ALTAR SET

Meissen (Johann Joachim Kaendler), about 1737—1741.
Porcelain.

There are preserved:

Six altar candlesticks. The thorns of gilded bronze. 55·3, 54·5, 54·1, 55·7, 54·3, 54·4 cm; $21^3/_4$, $21^1/_2$, $21^1/_4$, 22, $21^1/_2$, $21^1/_2$ in. high. Meissen trade mark. (7079 to 7084)

St. John. 46·6 cm; $18^3/_8$ in. high. The left hand with the pen is missing. (7086)
St. Matthew. 47·2 cm; $18^5/_8$ in. high. (7087)
St. Andrew. 47·4 cm; $18^3/_4$ in. high. (7090)
St. James the elder. 46·2 cm; $18^1/_4$ in. high. (7095)
St. Simon. 46·7 cm; $18^3/_8$ in. high. Meissen trade-mark. (7091)
St. Bartholomew. 47·1 cm; $18^5/_8$ in. high. (7093)
St. Philip. 45·8 cm; 18 in. high. (7094)
St. Thomas. 46·8 cm; $18^3/_8$ in. high. (7096)
Bell. 16·6 cm; $6^1/_2$ in. high. (7101)
Holy water vessel. 29 cm; $11^3/_8$ in. long. (7107)

By commission of August III made for Empress Amalia, his mother-in-law, the widow of Emperor Joseph I. The figures of the apostles are diminutive representations of the marble statues in San Giovanni in Laterano, Rome. — The coat of arms on the bases belongs to Empress Amalia. See No. 150.

150   COMPLETIONS TO THE ALTAR SET No. 149

Vienna, beginning of the 19th century.

Lavabo porcelain.
a) Bowl: 32×27 cm; $12^5/_8 \times 10/^5_8$ in. The Meissen trade-mark painted (baked in an assay furnace) over the original mark (?) which was erased. (7109)
b) Can: 20 cm; $7^7/_8$ in. high. Meissen trade-mark later painted on and baked in an assay furnace. (7108)
Salver with two cruets. Porcelain.
a) Salver: $33·2 \times 25·8$ cm; $13^1/_8 \times 10^1/_8$ in. Red-white-red escutcheon, on top the Meissen trade-mark, baked in an assay furnace. Dated (1)802. Painter's mark P. (7103)
b) Cruets: Each 16·1 cm; $6^1/_4$ in. high. Dated 5. 9. (1)817. Painter's mark M. (or W). (7104, 7105)

Aspergile: Porcelain. 10 cm; $3^7/_8$ in. high. Meissen trade-mark baked in assay furnace. (7106)

Three Canon plates. Porcelain.
a) $36·9 \times 28$ cm; $14^1/_2 \times 11$ in. (7098) b) $19·2 \times 23$ cm; $7^1/_2 \times 9^1/_8$ in. (7099)
c) $19·1 \times 23$ cm; $7^1/_2 \times 9^1/_8$ in. (7100)

151   CRUCIFIX

Johann Baptist Hagenauer (born 1732 in Strass, Upper Bavaria, died 9th September 1810 at Vienna), 1757.

71 cm; 28 in. high. Lead; gray marble; wood. Signed: I. HAGENAUER INV(ENIT) ET FEC(IT) 1757, and I HAGENA. (E 50)

152   ST. FRANCIS SERAPHICUS

Laurent Delvaux (born 1696 at Ghent [?], died 1778 at Nivelles).

50·5 cm; $19^7/_8$ in. high. Carrara marble. Signed: L. DELVAUX S(VAE) C(AESA-REAE) M(AIESTATIS) SCVLPTOR FECIT. (D 93)

153 ST. THERESA OF AVILA
Laurent Delvaux (born 1696 at Ghent [?], died 1778 at Nivelles).
52 cm; 20¹/₂ in. high. Carrara marble. Signed: L. DEVAUX S(VAE) CAESA-
REAE) M(AIESTATIS) SCVLPTOR FECIT. (D 94)

VI. THE 19th CENTURY

154 BROWN CHASUBLE
German, 2nd half of the 18th century.
Brown silk with silk embroidery; silver orphreys. (A 216)

155 BLUE CHASUBLE
German, 2nd half of the 18th century.
Blue satin with silk embroidery; gold orphreys. (A 136)

156 RELIQUARY WITH A RELIC AND MINIATURE PORTRAIT OF
ST. FRANCIS SERAPHICUS
Pietro de Rossi (born 1761, died 1831 at St. Petersburg), 1793.
29·5 cm; 11⁵/₈ in. high. Silver; bronze, gilded; green marble; porphyry; ivory
miniature. Signed "de Rossi f.". (D 73)

157 RELIQUARY WITH A RELIC AND MINIATURE PORTRAIT OF
ST. THERESA OF AVILA
Pietro de Rossi (born 1761, died 1831 at St. Petersburg), 1793.
29·5 cm; 11⁵/₈ in. high. Silver; bronze, gilded; green marble; porphyry; ivory
miniature. Signed: "P. de Rossis f. 1793.". (D 74)

158 ST. FRANZ OF PAULA SUMMONS THE COMMANDER-IN-CHIEF
JOHANNES COLOMY TO BATTLE AGAINST THE TURKS
Pietro de Rossi (born 1761, died 1831 at St. Petersburg), 1794.
14·4 × 27·5 cm; 5⁵/₈ × 10³/₄ in. Signed: "Pet(ru)s de Rubeis inu. et fecit
Rom(ae) 1794". (D 132)
With a small relic of the Saint. — Johannes Colomy was the commander-in-
chief of King Ferdinand I of Sicily (1468—1516).

159 PACIFICALE
Vienna (?), 1777.
21·6 cm; 8¹/₂ in. high. Gold; gilded silver. Viennese gold and silver remarks
1806/07, remark for silver 1809/10. (D 102)

160 "MARIAN" VESTMENT
Austrian, about 1819—1831.
Silver lamé with gold embroidery. (A 47)
With the arms of Archduke Cardinal Rudolf (1788—1831), Prince Archbishop
of Olmütz.

161 BLUE CHASUBLE
Vienna, around 1835.
Light blue velvet with silver embroidery; silver orphreys. (A 181)

Ordered by Empress Caroline Augusta for the chapel that was established in the room where Emperor Franz I of Austria died.

162   RED CHASUBLE
Vienna, around 1835.
Scarlet velvet with gold embroidery; gold orphreys. (A 184)
Cf. No. 161.

163   WHITE CHASUBLE
Vienna, around 1835.
White satin with gold embroidery; gold orphreys. (A 183)
Cf. No. 161.

164   GREEN CHASUBLE
Vienna, around 1835.
Green velvet with silver embroidery. Silver orphreys.
Cf. No. 161.

165   CRUCIFIX
Rome (?), 1815—1823.
48 cm; 19 in. high. Steel; wooden base; gold bronze. (E 11)
In the base a golden casket (13·1 × 3·4 cm; 5¹/₄ × 13³/₈ in., 5·1 cm; 2 in. high.

Roman town-mark, maker's mark 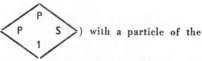) with a particle of the

Cross and relics of Saints Peter and Paul. Gift of Pope Pius VII to Emperor Franz I of Austria.

166   CHALICE AND PATEN
Heinrich Kern, Vienna, 1840.
Chalice 28·4 cm; 11¹/₄ in. high. Gilded silver. Viennese town-mark 1840, maker's mark K in a rhomb. (B 24)
On chalice and paten the coat of arms of Emperor Ferdinand I.

167   CENSER AND TRAY
Heinrich Kern, Vienna, 1824.
Viennese town-mark 1824, maker's mark K in a rhomb. (C 35)
On both vessels the coat of arms of Habsburg-Lorraine.

168   TWO CRUETS WITH SALVER
J. Kern, Vienna, 1835.
Salver 26·2 × 17 cm; 10¹/₄ × 6⁷/₈ in., cruets 13 cm; 5¹/₈ in. high. Silver. Viennese town-mark 1835, maker's mark I. KERN. (C 200)

169   "JUBILEE" VESTMENT
Vienna, 1849.
Gold cloth with gold embroidery. (A 22)
On the chasuble the monograms F. I and M. A, the year number 1849 and the Imperial double eagle with the coat of arms of Habsburg-Lorraine.

Donated by Emperor Ferdinand I and Empress Maria Anna on the occasion of the quatercentary celebration of the consecration of the Castle Chapel (28th April 1849).

170 BISHOP'S CROSSES AND RINGS OF THE COURT BISHOP DR. LAURENZ MAYER (in Court service 1876—1913)

    a) Pectoral with chain. Gold; topazes; brilliants; diamonds. Maker's mark FR in a rhomb. (C 303)
        The chain: maker's mark ⎡B & L⎤ . (C 303)

    b) Pectoral with chain. Gold; amethysts; diamonds. (C 304)
        The chain: maker's mark ⎡BS⎤ . (C 304)

    c) Pectoral. Gold; amethysts; diamonds. Maker's mark M. Kersch, Prague. (C 317)

    d) Chain. Gold. Maker's mark (A S) . (C 314)

    e) Pontifical ring. Gold; topaz; diamonds. (C 308)
        According to the inventory a memento to Crown Prince Rudolph.

    f) Pontifical ring. Gold; amethyst; brilliants; diamonds. (C 306)
        In the case the firm's mark "A. E. Köchert, Wien". — Gift of Empress Elizabeth on the occasion of the baptism of Archduchess Ella.

    g) Pontifical ring. Gold; amethyst; diamonds. (C 318)
        In the case the firm's mark "Matzenauer, k. k. Hofjuwelier, Wien".

171 OSTENSORY WITH A TOOTH OF ST. PETER
Rome (?), probably 1853.

78·5 cm; 31 in. high. Silver, partly gilded; bronze; lapis lazuli; diamonds; rubies; aquamarines; amethysts; hyacinths; emeralds; sapphires; topazes. (D 45)

Gift of Pope Pius IX to Emperor Franz Joseph I after the latter's lucky escape from an attempt on his life in 1853.

172 CUPBOARD HOLDING THE KEYS TO THE COFFINS OF HABSBURGS (XVI A 24)
Alexander Albert, Court carpenter, Vienna, 1895.

For the burial of members of the Imperial House the following ceremony has been handed down: after the funeral train had reached the vault of the Capucine Church in Vienna, the coffin was opened, whereupon the Grand Chamberlain asked the father Guardian of the Capucine convent whether he recognized the dead person. After the affirmative answer, the coffin was shut with two locks; one key was given to the father Guardian and the other kept in the Treasure chamber. Only later was the coffin laid in the magnificent sarcophagus. — In addition, the keys of the coffins of Habsburgs who are buried in Linz, Gmünd, Bolzano, Gran and Mantua also came to the Treasure chamber, and finally also the key to the vault in the Monastery of Seckau (Styria). When the vault of Neuberg (Styria) was renovated in 1870/71, and subsequently in 1898 new metal coffins were ordered for the Habsburgs resting there, the new keys were also kept in the Treasure chamber. Thus the longest dead person whose coffin-key is kept here is Duke Otto the Gay († 1339). The middle section of the cupboard is reserved for the Emperors and their close relatives, the keys to the coffins of all the other archdukes are kept at the sides. Altogether the chest holds the keys to 139 coffins. Most of the keys are of fairly recent origin. The oldest date back to the 17th century. — The ivory crucifix is a German work from the 2nd third of the 17th century. (XIV 33)

INDEX OF ARTISTS

The first number indicates the corresponding page; separated by a diagonal stroke there follows the catalogue number. Numbers of pages are separated by semicolons, catalogue numbers by commas.

1. The crown of the Holy Roman Empire (Nr. 152)

2. The imperial cross, detail (Nr. 156)

3. The imperial cross (Nr. 156)

4. The "sabre of Charlemagne", detail (Nr. 162)

5. The imperial sword, detail (Nr. 155)

6. The coronation mantle (Nr. 163)

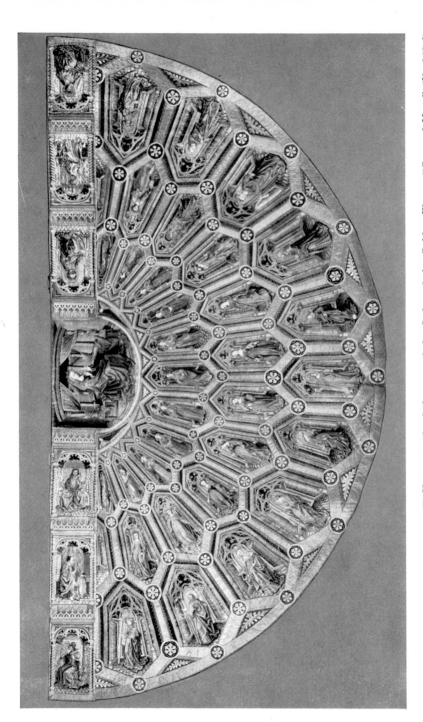

7. Vestments for holy man of the Order of the Golden Fleece, "Cope of Mary" (Nr. 143 d)

8. Vestments for holy man of the Order of the Golden Fleece,
   Altar antependium, detail (Nr. 143 a)

9. Brooch (Nr. 150)

10. The swearing-in cross of the order of the Golden Fleece (Nr. 144)

11. The Burgundian court goblet (Nr. 147)

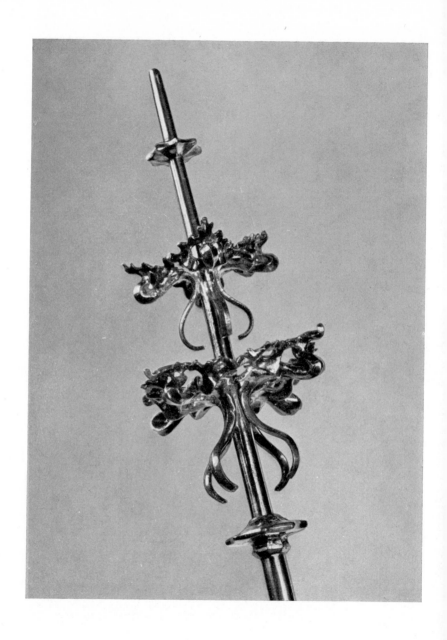

12. The insignia of hereditary homage, sceptre, detail (Nr. 3)

13. The orb of emperor Mathias, the imperial orb of Austria (Nr. 56)

14. The Austrian imperial crown (Nr. 55)

15. Emperor Franz I of Austria with the Austrian imperial mantle,
by F. v. Amerling (Nr. 68)

16. Hyacinth "La Bella" (Nr. 105)

17. The crown of Stephan Bocskay (Nr. 59)

18. Tabard of the herald of the order of the Fleece (No. 18)

19. Tabard of the herold of the Roman Emperor (Nr. 62)

20. The Austrian imperial mantle, detail (Nr. 69)

21. The cradle of the King of Rome (Nr. 119)

22. The baptismal can (Nr. 45)

23. Golden rose tree (Nr. 113)

24. Small family-altar (Nr. 48)

25. Small family-altar (Nr. 58)

26. J. B. Känischbauer, Pacificale (Nr. 125)

27. J. Moser, Chalice (Nr. 129)

28. Golden Chasuble (Nr. 108)

29. The so-called Parrots vestment, cope (Nr. 132)

30. M. Steinle, Crucificion-Group, detail (Nr. 122)

31. J. J. Kaendler, St. Matthew (Nr. 149)

32. J. B. Hagenauer, Crucifix (Nr. 151)